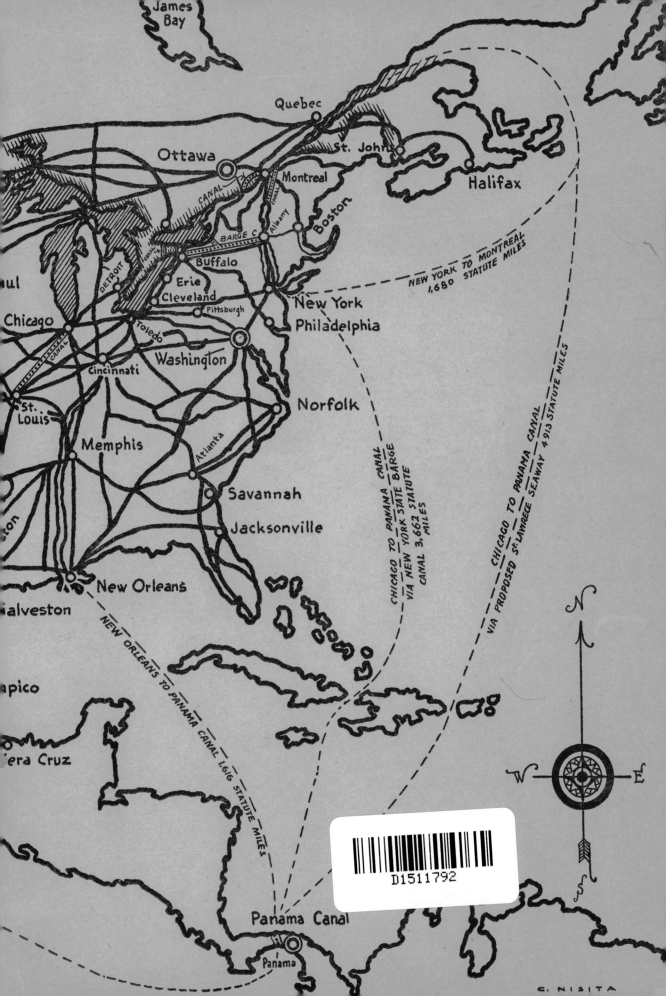

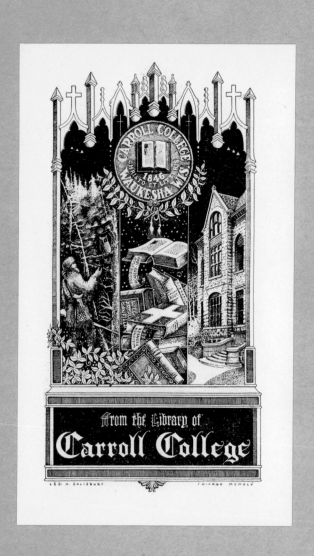

The St. Lawrence Seaway Project

By

B. D. TALLAMY
T. M. SEDWEEK

NIAGARA FRONTIER PLANNING BOARD

Buffalo, New York

1940

Printed in the U. S. A.
at
THE ROYCROFT SHOPS
East Aurora, N. Y.

NIAGARA FRONTIER PLANNING BOARD

✓ ✓ ✓

THE Niagara Frontier Planning Board is the first official regional planning agency to be established in the United States. It was created under Chapter 267 of the Laws of 1925 of the State of New York.

By this statute the Board is directed to study the needs and conditions of regional and community planning in Erie and Niagara Counties and prepare plans adapted to meet such needs and conditions. Through such agencies as it may designate, the Board may collect and distribute information relative to regional and community planning in Erie and Niagara Counties.

This, of necessity, requires a study of all proposals which have an effect upon the economic, social, industrial and physical development of the Frontier.

The Planning Board is composed of the mayors of the six cities in Erie and Niagara Counties, together with six supervisors, three appointed by the Erie County Board of Supervisors, and three appointed by the Niagara County Board of Supervisors. These twelve elect a private citizen as Chairman of the Board.

The following is the personnel of the Niagara Frontier Planning Board:

Mayor Thomas L. Holling, Buffalo
Mayor Ernest W. Mirrington, Niagara Falls
Mayor John E. Aszkler, Lackawanna
Mayor Edward H. Gailor, Lockport
Mayor John E. Wallace, North Tonawanda
Mayor Christ S. Warren, Tonawanda

Supervisor Leslie F. Robinson,
    Town of Aurora
Supervisor Carl E. Sentz,
    City of Tonawanda
Supervisor William J. McMahon,
    City of Buffalo

Supervisor George S. Grimm,
    City of North Tonawanda
Supervisor Louis M. Hageman,
    City of Niagara Falls
Supervisor John H. Northrup,
    City of Niagara Falls

Chauncey J. Hamlin
Chairman

B. D. Tallamy, *Chief Engineer*   T. M. Sedweek, *Executive Secretary*

ACKNOWLEDGEMENTS

✔ ✔ ✔

THE compilation of this report would not have been possible without assistance from many sources. Various individuals and public and private agencies throughout the country have lent their efforts to enable the gathering of the material. It is unfortunate that space is insufficient to permit the recognition of all these by name.

Perforce, the listing of acknowledgements is restricted to the Niagara Frontier, but to others as well as to these herewith mentioned the Niagara Frontier Planning Board tacitly expresses its appreciation.

The Boards of Supervisors of Erie and Niagara Counties, New York, the City Councils of Buffalo, Niagara Falls, Lockport, Lackawanna, Tonawanda and North Tonawanda, the Buffalo Courier-Express and the Buffalo Evening News, the Committee of One Hundred, the Niagara Frontier Planning Association and the Buffalo Chamber of Commerce and the Port of Buffalo Defense Committee have given valuable support in this work.

To the authors of the report, B. D. Tallamy, Chief Engineer for the Planning Board, and T. M. Sedweek, Executive Secretary for the Planning Board, the members of the Board are particularly indebted. The Board also wishes to acknowledge the effective work of the authors' colleagues, Gordon E. Brown, the Board's Publicity Director; Wallace V. R. Fretts, who assisted in making the technical study on the power portion of the St. Lawrence Seaway and Power Project, and Ray C. Hoffman, who assisted in making the statistical survey on traffic movements in connection with the navigation portion of the project.

Chauncey J. Hamlin, Chairman
NIAGARA FRONTIER PLANNING BOARD

✔

SOURCES OF FUNDS

All activities of the Niagara Frontier Planning Board are financed by public funds. Appropriations to finance this study of the St. Lawrence Project and the publication and distribution of the findings were made by the Counties of Erie and Niagara and the Cities of Buffalo, Niagara Falls, Tonawanda and North Tonawanda, New York.

PREFACE

✱ ✱ ✱

THIS report on the widely-discussed St. Lawrence Project has been prepared by the Executive Staff of the Niagara Frontier Planning Board at the direction of the Board. Because of the Niagara Frontier's intimate geographic and economic ties with any large-scale development in the St. Lawrence-Niagara Falls-Great Lakes area, the Board deemed it wise, as a planning function, to make a thorough report on that project.

The Executive Staff was instructed to conduct the research on a comprehensive scale and thus determine the effects of the proposed seaway and power undertaking on the nation at large. While the plan obviously has certain spacial limitations and therefore would not affect all territorial sections with equal intensity, it nevertheless would be a gigantic international project and would involve huge expenditures by the federal treasuries of two countries.

For these reasons, the St. Lawrence proposal concerns commercial, industrial and financial interests over a vast terrain. As a federal venture, it spreads the United States share of the costs throughout the entire country. In no sense is the matter of purely local consequence. Every American has a financial interest in it.

The findings of this survey unequivocally demonstrate that the St. Lawrence Project would be exceedingly detrimental to the United States, the State of New York and the Niagara Frontier. They show that even if any advantages should accrue to the public through the contemplated hydroelectric power development, these benefits could not warrant the disastrous consequences of the proposed navigation works.

The Planning Board has carefully reviewed this report of its Executive Staff and has unanimously concurred in the findings. It has authorized the printing of this report for distribution throughout the country. The Board believes that the survey, showing the threats to existing transportation facilities, to ports, terminals and affiliated industries as well as to American labor and the American taxpayer, should prompt immediate and decisive disapproval of the St. Lawrence Project.

NIAGARA FRONTIER PLANNING BOARD
Chauncey J. Hamlin, *Chairman*

INTRODUCTION

✶ ✶ ✶

SINCE 1909, certain interests in Canada and the United States have been constantly at work developing arguments both for and against construction of the Great Lakes-St. Lawrence Seaway and Power Project. At this writing, the Administration in Washington reportedly is planning to submit a new treaty, calling for the St. Lawrence development, to the Canadian government.

In the preparation of this survey, the basic materials used were the reports of a Joint Board of Engineers (appointed by the Canadian and United States governments), an Interdepartmental Report of the United States Government, other governmental documents, and the report published by the Brookings Institution, an impartial research foundation of Washington, D. C. Original analyses as to the costs and as to the economic and political effects of the proposed seaway were then made from this basic material. Data from such sources were believed to be the most authentic information on the subject.

Of necessity, this study has reached out far beyond the confines of the Niagara Frontier, because every port along the Great Lakes and the major ports of the Atlantic and Pacific Oceans and the Gulf of Mexico, the railroads, inland waterways, highways and closely allied industries would be vitally influenced.

The report, which carries a summary for each chapter, includes:

(1)   A list of the major findings.

(2)   A brief history of the project.

(3)   A discussion, section by section, of the proposed Treaty of 1938.

(4)   A description of the proposed seaway as related to existing facilities.

(5)   A discussion of costs of the navigation project.

(6)   A discussion of the navigation project in relation to savings in shipping rates as contrasted with losses to existing transportation and allied industrial interests in the United States.

(7)   A description of the power project, its cost and savings.

(8)   The appendices, containing the authority for transportation rates used in this report and a copy of the proposed treaty of 1938.

For the sake of convenience, the major findings are briefly presented in the immediately following paragraphs. Ready references to the detailed discussions from which the conclusions were drawn are also listed for the convenience of readers wishing promptly to study in detail the methods of arriving at the conclusions.

MAJOR FINDINGS

General Conclusion: This economic survey of the *St. Lawrence Seaway and New York State-Ontario Power Project conclusively demonstrates the proposed development, considered in its entirety as an undertaking which includes navigation as well as power works, to be unsound. The seaway would be so generally ruinous to American commerce and industry, labor and capital, that its nation-wide deleterious effects would far exceed whatever claimed advantages might redound to certain special interests from the waterway or to New York State and the Province of Ontario from the power plan. The following findings tell why:

The minimum total cost of the whole St. Lawrence project for both the United States and Canada would be $1,120,588,000: This figure is founded on government estimates. It is about three times the cost of the Panama Canal. (See page 34).

The St. Lawrence project, on the basis of experience with similar works, probably would cost more than the $1,120,588,000: A total of $375,000,-000 was spent on the Panama Canal, although it had been estimated to cost only $160,000,000, the Chicago Sanitary and Ship Canal cost $53,000,000 instead of $16,000,000 and the Suez Canal cost $80,000,000 instead of $30,000,000. (See page 32).

At least 85% of the United States share of the project's cost would be borne by American taxpayers who would be the victims of unfair discrimination: These taxpayers live in the region which could not be benefited by the St. Lawrence seaway even if claims of proponents were valid. (See page 38).

American labor, transportation and industry, on the government's estimates of probable seaway traffic, would lose $109,647,000 a year: Diversion of business from American transportation systems to foreign carriers, diversion of Canadian export grain movement from the United States and loss to American coal producers account for this figure. (See pages 82-88).

The net loss to the United States would be $76,595,000 each year on the basis of the government's estimates of seaway traffic: This sum represents the difference between two factors: one is the loss to established American commerce and industry plus the expense to American taxpayers; the other is the possible rate saving by shipping via the St. Lawrence. (See page 88).

---

*The project is popularly known simply as the St. Lawrence Seaway and Power Project. A more appropriate title, however, is the one used here: the St. Lawrence Seaway and New York State-Ontario Power Project. The latter is more explanatory because, while the seaway would affect large regions throughout the United States and Canada, the St. Lawrence power development, as planned in the international scheme, would supply hydro-electric energy only to the State of New York and the Province of Ontario.

During 42% of the year, the St. Lawrence seaway could not be fully utilized: The route would be closed because of ice conditions. (See page 41).

The American farmer would not gain from the St. Lawrence seaway: Export grain would be the chief American agricultural product to be shipped through the waterway. Even if a possible maximum saving of 3 cents a bushel were realized, this would be absorbed by the foreign purchaser and vessel-owner. (See page 62).

American manufacturers, who have cultivated this country's great inland market, would be seriously damaged by foreign competition resulting from the St. Lawrence seaway: Alien tramp steamers would dump cheaply produced commodities on this currently protected Great Lakes market. (See pages 56, 78, 81).

Foreign tramp ships would have almost exclusive use of the St. Lawrence seaway: American-owned vessels of sufficiently shallow draft to ply the proposed waterway comprise only 5% of the world's merchant ship tonnage. (See page 45).

No route for more profitable trade between American ports would be offered by the St. Lawrence seaway: The location of the St. Lawrence is such that no appreciable coastal or intercoastal commerce would occur. (See pages 89, 90, 91).

The St. Lawrence seaway would not carry the volume of traffic nor bring the savings in shipping rates to the exaggerated degree cited by many proponents: They have set the probable tonnage at 11,496,000 and the probable savings at $45,516,000 annually. The more accurate estimate is 3,873,000 for tonnage and $8,822,000 for savings. (See pages 72-80).

The net loss each year to American commerce and industry and to the American taxpayer, on the basis of more accurate figures for estimated tonnages and savings, would be $42,233,000: The United States investment in the St. Lawrence waterway would result in lower earnings and higher taxes. (See page 80).

Maintenance of wholly cordial relations between the United States and Canada might be endangered by the St. Lawrence seaway: Serious questions could arise as to responsibility for defense of the waterway in times of war and as to preservation of water-levels in Canadian harbors on the lower St. Lawrence River. (See page 12, 14).

Surrender of United States sovereignty over Lake Michigan would result from any treaty which, like the proposed treaty of 1938, limited the withdrawal of water from the lake at Chicago: It would prevent further development of the Great Lakes-Gulf of Mexico waterway by the United States. (See page 13).

The proposal for restoration of Niagara Falls beauty and for further power generation there has been inexcusably made contingent on the whole St. Lawrence project: There is no engineering demand for tying up the needed Niagara Falls project with the St. Lawrence development. (See pages 15, 116).

The United States would subsidize Canadian power to the extent of $48,860,000: This figure is reached by taking the minimum cost ($90,000,000) for the Canadian share of the power, under the least expensive plan yet advanced, and deducting costs strictly chargeable to power ($41,140,000), under the present plan. (See pages 117-118).

It is perfectly practical to divorce the seaway and power portions of the general St. Lawrence plan: There is no justification for burdening the proposed power development with the unsound seaway proposal. (See pages 95, 116).

The amount of power which would be created on the United States side of the river for $206,065,000 under the present St. Lawrence scheme could be produced for only $90,000,000 without the navigation project: The St. Lawrence Power Development Commission set $90,000,000 as a reasonable cost of power works on the American side of the International Rapids Section. (See page 95).

Whatever power benefits might result from the St. Lawrence project would affect only the state of New York and Eastern Canada: The St. Lawrence plan does not envision sale of United States power beyond the confines of New York State. (See pages 4, 5, 96, 111, 112, 113).

Neither New York City nor Western New York is a practical market for St. Lawrence power: Under existing delivery conditions, power from nearer sources is more practical and economical for these areas. (See pages 100, 104).

Previous estimates of increased power demand in New York State are too optimistic: The Niagara Frontier Planning Board finds that the demand in 1952 probably will not exceed 21,000,000,000 kilowatt-hours (See page 114).

Over development of hydro-electric power is a dangerous policy to pursue: When generating plants are built without an adequate market for the power, the capital charges accumulate to such an extent that the project never pays. (See pages 115, 116).

Adequate and economical power potentialities, apart from the St. Lawrence river, exist today in New York State and Eastern Canada: Two outstanding examples are the Ottawa River in Canada and Niagara Falls. (See page 118).

Progressive development of Niagara Falls power potentialities independent of the seaway and in step with power needs is the most practical plan: This would eliminate economic hazards to the new developments and to existing plants. (See page 116).

The
ST. LAWRENCE SEAWAY
PROJECT

HISTORY

, , .

The River

STRETCHING nearly 1200 miles from the eastern end of Lake Ontario to the Atlantic Ocean, the St. Lawrence River is one of the world's most magnificent waterways. It has diversity in its beauty, for this masterpiece of nature first races turbulently through a series of boiling rapids and then becomes calm when it reaches Montreal to flow placidly to the sea.

The physical grandeur of the river, however, does not necessarily endow it with the manifold factors that must exist if a seaway project, connecting the Great Lakes with the Atlantic Ocean, is to be economically justified.

Over its first 110 miles, from its beginning at Lake Ontario, the St. Lawrence divides the United States from the Dominion of Canada. Then it becomes a wholly Canadian river for the balance of its stretch northeast to the ocean. Fourteen-foot-deep Canadian canals now circumvent the narrow rapids sections between Lake Ontario and Montreal, while 30-foot-deep channels exist in the river bed between Montreal and the Atlantic.

The St. Lawrence, serving as a gigantic drain for the Great Lakes basin, is not always a freely flowing river, though, because when winter comes to this waterway, ice comes too. With the arrival of cold weather, navigation ceases and the river is locked in a frigid grip for some five months each year.

Whether it is economically feasible to construct elaborate works, so that ocean-going ships may pass into the Great Lakes through 27-foot-deep canals during the open season, is the question at hand. In reaching an answer, the practicalities of the problem must be winnowed from the confusing elements of wishful dreaming that always accompany such colossal projects.

In the following pages, an analysis determines how well reasoned are the plans for developing the St. Lawrence. Is it wise for man to expend further energy and money on this river? Would the project mean economic progress or economic retrogression, in the light of limitations imposed by nature and of man's present investment in other transportation media?

The search for these answers logically begins with historical background.

The International Line

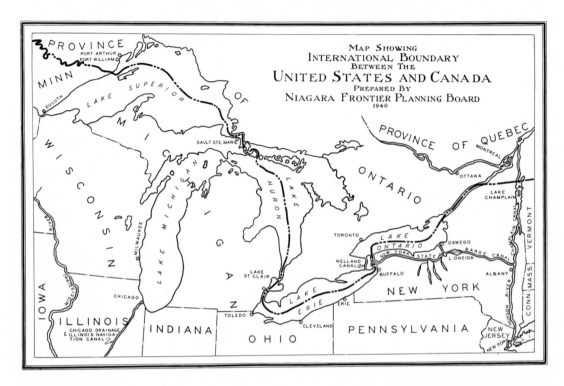

MAP SHOWING
INTERNATIONAL BOUNDARY
BETWEEN THE
UNITED STATES AND CANADA
PREPARED BY
NIAGARA FRONTIER PLANNING BOARD
1940

A boundary between Canada and the United States was established by treaty in 1783. Later, in writing the treaty of peace after the War of 1812, the commissioners of the United States and Great Britain reaffirmed the boundary which had been established by the first treaty. The international line thus agreed upon, running through the St. Lawrence River and Great Lakes System, was essentially the same as we now know it. The following is a quotation from the Treaty of 1812:

> "Thence (from the point where the 45th parallel of north Latitude westward first meets the St. Lawrence) along the middle of the said river, into Lake Ontario; through the middle of said lake until it strikes the communication by water between that lake and Lake Erie; thence along the middle of said communication, into Lake Erie; through the middle of said lake, until it arrives at the water communication between that lake and Lake Huron; thence along the middle of said water communication, into Lake Huron; thence through the middle of said lake, to the water communication between that lake and Lake Superior; thence through Lake Superior northward of the isles Royals and Philipeaux, to the Long Lake; thence through the middle of said Long Lake, and the water communication between it and the Lake of the Woods, to the Lake of the Woods; thence, through the said lake, to the most northwestern point thereof."

Use of Boundary Waters: The perpetual right of the United States to use the waters of the St. Lawrence below the international boundary as a navigation route from the Great Lakes to the ocean was given by a treaty in 1871.

Under provisions of a treaty signed by Canada and the United States in 1909, the International Joint Commission was created in 1911 as a permanent body to deal with the use, obstruction or diversion of boundary waters.

These treaties left Lake Michigan and its entire watershed in American territory; it could not be considered in any way a "boundary water." From that time to the present there has never been any question as to our national rights in these waters. It is well to keep this fact in mind while this latest proposal for a St. Lawrence development is analyzed.

The Deep Waterway Idea is Born

The movement for the creation of a deep waterway of 184 statute miles from Montreal to the foot of Lake Ontario and thence for some 1164 statute miles through the Great Lakes to Duluth gained major impetus in 1919. In that year the Great Lakes-St. Lawrence Tidewater Association was formed to promote the project. During the same year an amendment to the Rivers and Harbors Act was passed requesting an investigation and report on the costs of further improvements of the St. Lawrence between Montreal and Lake Ontario in order to make the river navigable for ocean-going vessels.

Commissions and Boards Appointed to Study the Proposal: Since that time, various other commissions, departments and committees have made reports on the subject.

In 1920, the International Joint Commission was asked to report on the necessary improvements for navigation alone and also for a combination of navigation and power works. At the same time the two governments appointed a Board of Engineers to assist the International Joint Commission.

In December, 1921, this Commission submitted a report recommending improvement of the St. Lawrence river. In this they approved a depth of 25 feet in the canals and 30 feet over lock sills, the estimated cost of recommended improvements being placed at $252,728,000. No official action, however, was taken in regard to this recommendation.

The St. Lawrence Commission, under the chairmanship of the Honorable Herbert Hoover, then Secretary of Commerce, was appointed in 1924 by President Coolidge for the purpose of advising on the economic feasibility of the proposed deep waterway. About the same time, a National Advisory Committee was appointed by Canada to report to the Dominion Government. Also, a Joint Board of Engineers, consisting of three Americans and three Canadians, was appointed to review the engineering report of 1921 and consider further questions submitted by the governments.

Reports Submitted: The Joint Board of Engineers estimated the total eventual cost of improvements, consisting of a 25-foot channel and fully developed power resources in the St. Lawrence between Lake Ontario and Montreal, at from $620,000,000 to $650,000,000, depending upon the type of improvement adopted in the International Rapids Section. In addition, there was an estimated cost of $45,000,000 for improving Great Lakes Channels above Lake Ontario to a depth of 25 feet; the total improvements recommended for immediate development were estimated to cost from $350,000,000 to $385,000,000.

The Department of Commerce made a survey of the comparative merits and probable costs of the St. Lawrence seaway, the Great Lakes-Hudson River project and a proposed all-American route. The Great Lakes-Hudson route would require the construction of a deep waterway from Oswego, N. Y., on Lake Ontario to the Hudson River, via the Erie Canal and Oswego Canal. Another alternate considered was a deep waterway along the St. Lawrence River to Lake St. Francis and thence south to Lake Champlain and the Hudson River. The all-American route would be the same as the Oswego-Erie Canal route except that it would call for an American canal around Niagara Falls on American territory and then follow the Oswego-to-Hudson River route. The American routes, alternate to the St. Lawrence Seaway, were not favorably considered because of greater costs.

Following the submission of these findings, the St. Lawrence Commission made its report in 1926 favoring the immediate improvement of the St. Lawrence for navigation and power purposes, provided a suitable agreement could be made with Canada for the joint undertaking. In this report, the Commission recommended that "the United States should recognize the proper relations of New York to the power development in the International Section" and stressed the significance of the St. Lawrence route from the transportation point of view.

Canada's Views on the Subject

The Department of State, in April, 1927, presented the conclusions of the St. Lawrence Commission to the Canadian Government and expressed the desire of the United States to enter into negotiations for the development of the project.

The Canadian Government, however, asked for a postponement of the matter until after the completion and release of the appendices to the Joint Engineers' Report.

In January, 1928, the Dominion Government transmitted to the Department of State its views on the seaway project and the findings of its National Advisory Committee. These views covered two points, i. e., the conditions under which the Canadian Government could be in a position to enter into negotiations for a treaty for the development of the St. Lawrence, and an explanation of the various transportation facilities and factors in Canada which differ decidedly from those of the United States.

Dominion Government Feels Negotiations Premature: The Dominion Government stated frankly it felt negotiations were premature at that time and suggested that the case then before the Supreme Court of Canada, regarding the water power rights of the Dominion Government and of the Provinces, be settled first. Canada also urged that the engineers of the two countries reach an agreement on the project for improvement of the International Rapids Section of the river. The United States representatives on the Joint Board of Engineers had recommended development of the International Rapids Section in a single stage, while the Canadian members of the Joint Board of Engineers had recommended a two stage development. In connection with this difference of opinion, the Canadian Government further stated in its note that:

> "It is also advisable that opportunity should be afforded for further conference on these alternative proposals between the Canadian section of the Joint Board and engineers representing the Province of Ontario, who have themselves formulated plans dealing with the international section."

Following these preliminary steps, Canada expressed herself as ready to cooperate with the United States on a deep waterway project provided Canada would not be required to develop her share of hydro-electric power in advance of the growth of her market to absorb it and provided the Dominion Government would not be required to undertake heavy financial burdens for the project.

The State of New York Enters the Picture

In 1930, the State of New York appointed the St. Lawrence Power Development Commission to investigate the power possibilities of the river contiguous to New York State. On January 15, 1931, this Commission reported to the Governor of the State in favor of public power development at the International Section of the St. Lawrence River.

The Power Authority of the State of New York: The Power Authority of the State of New York was created by an act of the State Legislature in 1931. On February 7, 1933, this agency and the United States Engineers recommended that the costs for which the United States would be responsible in connection with the development of the International Rapids Section of the St. Lawrence River should be divided between the United States and the State of New York. New York's share was set at $89,726,000. For this payment, New York State was to have the right to utilize, for power development, all of the St. Lawrence River flow in the International Rapids Section allocated to the United States by treaty, other than that required for navigation. The State of New York was also to receive title to the power works and lands upon which they were located, and which might be necessary and convenient for their operation.

Treaty Signed

On July 18, 1932, a treaty between the United States, Canada and Great Britain was signed to effectuate the project. It was then submitted to the United States Senate for ratification.

Further Investigations: From November, 1932, to February, 1933, the Committee on Foreign Affairs of the United States Senate conducted an exhaustive investigation on the treaty. From that point until March, 1934, there was lengthy discussion in the Senate both for and against the St. Lawrence Seaway Project.

Treaty Rejected by United States Senate: Finally, on March 14th, 1934, the St. Lawrence Treaty was rejected by the United States Senate.

The Senate based its disapproval upon the mass of testimony presented in opposition to the project, testimony which indicated great injury to the established transportation systems of the United States and destruction of property values in ports along the Atlantic coast, the Great Lakes and the Gulf of Mexico. The Senate also considered the unfair and detrimental effects on other sections of the country where tax increases would have been necessary to support the St. Lawrence plan.

There were 88 members in the Senate when a vote on the question was called. The roll call resulted in 46 yeas and 42 nays. Because treaty ratification requires a two-thirds vote, the proposal was lost. The following table gives the specific votes:

TABLE I

Senatorial Votes on the St. Lawrence Seaway Treaty, March 14, 1934

Yeas—46

STATE	SENATOR	STATE	SENATOR
Alabama	Bankhead	Nebraska	Thompson
Alabama	Black	Nevada	Pittman
Arizona	Ashurst	New Hampshire	Brown
Arizona	Hayden	New Mexico	Cutting
Arkansas	Robinson	New Mexico	Hatch
California	Johnson	North Dakota	Frazier
California	McAdoo	North Dakota	Nye
Colorado	Costigan	Ohio	Bulkley
Idaho	Borah	Ohio	Fess
Idaho	Pope	Oklahoma	Gore
Indiana	Van Nuys	South Carolina	Byrnes

Yeas (Concluded)

STATE	SENATOR	STATE	SENATOR
Indiana	Robinson	South Carolina	Smith
Kansas	Capper	South Dakota	Bulow
Kentucky	Barkley	Tennessee	Bachman
Kentucky	Logan	Tennessee	McKellar
Michigan	Couzens	Texas	Sheppard
Michigan	Vandenberg	Utah	Thomas
Minnesota	Schall	Vermont	Gibson
Minnesota	Shipstead	Washington	Bone
Mississippi	Harrison	Washington	Dill
Montana	Erickson	Wisconsin	Duffy
Montana	Wheeler	Wisconsin	LaFollette
Nebraska	Norris	Wyoming	O'Mahoney

Nays—42

STATE	SENATOR	STATE	SENATOR
Colorado	Adams	Nevada	McCarran
Connecticut	Walcott	New Hampshire	Keyes
Connecticut	Lonergan	New Jersey	Kean
Delaware	Hastings	New Jersey	Barbour
Delaware	Townsend	New York	Wagner
Georgia	George	New York	Copeland
Georgia	Russell	North Carolina	Bailey
Illinois	Dieterich	North Carolina	Reynolds
Illinois	Lewis	Oregon	McNary
Iowa	Dickinson	Oregon	Steiwer
Kansas	McGill	Pennsylvania	Davis
Louisiana	Long	Pennsylvania	Reed
Louisiana	Overton	Rhode Island	Hebert
Maine	Hale	Rhode Island	Metcalf
Maine	White	Texas	Connally
Maryland	Goldsborough	Virginia	Byrd
Maryland	Tydings	Vermont	Austin
Massachusetts	Coolidge	West Virginia	Hatfield
Massachusetts	Walsh	West Virginia	Neely
Mississippi	Stephens	Wyoming	Carey
Missouri	Patterson		
Missouri	Clark		

Not Voting—8

STATE	SENATOR	STATE	SENATOR
Arkansas	Caraway	Oklahoma	Thomas
Florida	Fletcher	South Dakota	Norbeck
Florida	Trammell	Utah	King
Iowa	Murphy	Virginia	Glass

A New Treaty is Offered: On May 28, 1938, the United States, through its Secretary of State, submitted to Canada a new form of treaty providing for a St. Lawrence seaway and incidental power developments. This time, the opposition seemed to be of greater volume than in the past. Premier Hepburn of Ontario and Premier Duplessis of Quebec definitely stated their opposition to the project and it looked as though it would be buried for all time. Later, however, there were indications that Premier Hepburn had changed his attitude. Perhaps the reason for this change was Mr. Hepburn's ultimate conviction that under the project the United States would be called upon to pay an undue proportion of the cost of developing the International Rapids Section of the seaway and thereby offer Canada an opportunity which might not again be available.

If the province of Ontario wished to defer Canadian development of the International Rapids Section, then the cost to the Dominion Government, or the Province of Ontario, would be only approximately $22,600,000 as compared with a United States cost of $144,000,000   (see table, page 38).

Summary of History

The question of whether the 1200-mile St. Lawrence River and the Great Lakes should be opened to ocean-going ships has been the object of advocacy or opposition by public and private groups for many years. Various government agencies have considered and reported on the matter at different times during the past two decades in this country. As this is being written, reports from Washington indicate that negotiations between the United States and the Dominion of Canada are again being held, and there is a probability that another St. Lawrence Treaty will be signed shortly.

Before the first treaty was consummated in 1932, the project had been considered by the International Joint Commission, the St. Lawrence Commission, the National Advisory Committee of Canada, the Joint Board of Engineers (consisting of three United States and three Dominion members), the St. Lawrence Power Development Commission, the New York State Power Authority and others.

But the United States Senate rejected the treaty in March, 1934, on grounds that the proposed St. Lawrence seaway was not generally desirable. This was almost seven years after the Joint Board of Engineers had estimated that construction of canals and channels between Lake Ontario and Montreal, with full hydro-electric power development, would cost between $620,000,000 and $650,000,000 as a total joint expense depending upon the type of improvement adopted for the International Rapids Section of the river.

The principal proponent in New York State of the St. Lawrence Seaway and Power Project today is the State Power Authority. In 1933,this agency joined the United States Engineers in recommending that the cost of works in the International Rapids Section be divided between New York State and the United States, with the Power Authority raising some $90,000,000 through the sale of bonds to reimburse the federal government.

Another treaty draft was offered Canada by this country in 1938, but the Province of Ontario was cool to the proposal at that time. Then, with the coming of the present European war last Fall, the Canadian attitude purportedly changed, and the whole St. Lawrence matter was revived in Washington.

PROPOSED TREATY OF 1938

Introduction — The Commission — Revision as to Project Costs — Divisions of Work — Advisory Capacity of Commission — Extension of Powers — Financial Obligations of Canada — Financial Obligations of the United States — Use of Water in International Rapids Section for Power — Proprietary Rights — Construction of Canal and Channel Facilities — Navigation Effect on Neutrality — United States Sovereignty over Lake Michigan — Further Remarks on the Sovereignty over Lake Michigan — Compensatory and Regulatory Works — Niagara Falls — Appointment of Special International Board — Damages and Ratification — Summary. (A complete copy of the treaty is in the appendices).

Introduction

THE following discussion is based upon the text of the treaty which was proposed by the United States government in 1938 and submitted to the Canadian government on May 28th of that year. This document is similar to the one signed by the two governments in 1932 and it is unlikely that there will be major changes in any treaty should one be consummated by the two governments in the near future.

Inasmuch as the international implications, the division of responsibilities and the costs of the project are largely determined by any treaty which may be signed by the two countries, it is necessary to study carefully the various provisions of the proposed Treaty of 1938 because that instrument is the basis of current discussions between the two governments.

Article I

The Commission: Article I of the treaty calls for the establishment of a Great Lakes-St. Lawrence Basin Commission consisting of not more than ten members of whom an equal number shall be appointed by each government. By an exchange of notes, the governments may change the number of members on the Commission, provided, however, that an equal representation of each government be maintained.

Revision as to Project Costs: Under this Article the treaty states that the Commission is to prepare plans in accordance with the Joint Board of Engineers' Report dated July 13th, 1927. It permits the Commission to make such modifications as may be agreed upon by the governments, provided those modifications do not increase the proposed total cost of the project as estimated in the aforementioned report.

This provision probably will be revised in the new treaty as the report of the Joint Board of Engineers, dated July 13, 1927, deals primarily with the two stage development of the International Rapids Section of the St. Lawrence River. All recent indications from Canada have been to the effect that the Canadian Government is now willing to proceed with a single stage plan of development. Inasmuch as the United States has always preferred the single stage development, it seems quite likely, in view of the changed Canadian opinion, that the new treaty will make mention of the single stage development and refer to the Joint Board of Engineers' Report of 1926 which considered that plan.

Divisions of Work: One of the duties of the Commission is to allocate construction to the two governments in such a way that each government shall construct the works within its own territory or an equivalent proportion in the International Rapids Section. As pointed out in Article III of the treaty, the United States has to pay for most of the work in the International Rapids Section. Therefore, according to the division of work as set forth in Article I, a large amount of work would be done by Canada with funds furnished by the United States. This work would accrue to the benefit of Canadian technicians, labor, materials and equipment.

In times like these, when there is such a serious unemployment situation in this country, every dollar expended by the United States government for construction work should result in a direct benefit to American labor and industry. This is particularly true in view of the fact that allowances are made to Canada for the moneys which were previously expended, or are to be expended, by her in the Canadian links of the seaway. If it is fair to divide the costs of all of the necessary links of the seaway, then it is equally fair to divide the labor benefits. American labor and industry did not share equally in the construction of the Welland Canal nor would they share equally in the construction of the canal project which lies wholly within Canada and downstream from the International Rapids Section. Provision for a more equitable distribution of labor benefits should be made a part of any new treaty.

Advisory Capacity of Commission: Article I also states that the Commission shall serve as an advisory group to the governments. They are to coordinate all plans relative to navigation and power in the entire Great Lakes-St. Lawrence Basin. While their authority in this connection is advisory, it is nevertheless important because the Commission, in this capacity, would supplant the Board of Army Engineers insofar as the United States is concerned.

Extension of Powers: Under this Article, the extension of the Commission's powers and duties is permitted through an international exchange of notes. In other words, without the protection offered by the formalities of a subsequent treaty, the powers of a Commission, established primarily to construct a definite project, may be enlarged to almost unlimited authority throughout the area of the Great Lakes and the St. Lawrence River.

Article II

Financial Obligations of Canada: An important part of Article II affects Canada rather than the United States. According to this Article, Canada must provide, not later than December 31, 1949, for the necessary additional development of the Welland Ship Canal and for completion of the entire Canadian section of the deep waterway to the sea.

This particular Article is extremely important. The people of Canada, in their assistance to the British Empire, are now facing their greatest period of financial stress. When one contemplates Canada's tremendous war expenses, her present enormous obligations, plus the annual deficits of the government-owned Canadian National Railway, one wonders how Canada can afford a further outlay of $240,601,000 (which over the amortization period would increase to $547,367,000) to create a competitor of this publicly-owned railway.

It is quite proper for the United States to have some concern over the ability of Canada to carry out her financial responsibilities (totalling over $179,000,000 in initial expenditures alone) under the proposed treaty. In case Canada should be forced to declare a moratorium, the United States would find herself in the position of having already spent approximately $144,000,000 to develop a link in a seaway which could not be used. Obviously it is necessary to have channels, canals and locks of the required depth both above and below the International Rapids Section if the works there are to be of any value as a navigation development. Should Canada be financially unable to complete her sections of the seaway project, this large expenditure of United States moneys would have been made with the sole effect of creating a power development for the Province of Ontario and the State of New York.

Article III

Financial Obligations of the United States: An important part of this Article is that the United States agrees to pay for all works in the International Rapids Section except Canadian power house superstructures, rehabilitation on the Canadian side, and any side canals and locks on the Canadian side.

Another important part of this Article is that the United States agrees to pay for and construct all other channel and compensating works in the Great Lakes system above Lake Erie.

Article IV

Use of Water in International Rapids Section for Power: In this Article, both countries agree that water for power purposes in the International Rapids Section shall be divided equally. However, Article VIII (d) stipulates that in the event one of the countries diverts water into the Great Lakes system or the St. Lawrence above the International Rapids Section, then that country is privileged to withdraw an additional equivalent amount for power purposes in the International Rapids Section.

The Province of Ontario has for some time wanted to divert water from Long Lake into Lake Superior. This would approximate 5000 cubic feet at Niagara Falls for power purposes. It would be of benefit to the Great Lakes System by improving water levels. Since, in this manner, the Province of Ontario would be benefiting rather than injuring navigation on the Great Lakes, certainly there is no reason for the United States to object. However, the United States has objected in the past on grounds that the Long Lake diversion should be contingent on Canadian approval of the seaway project.

Articles V & VI

Proprietary Rights: These Articles are not particularly controversial. Under Article V the countries agree that construction of the proposed works shall not confer upon either country proprietary rights or legislative, administrative or other jurisdiction in the territory of the other. It also states that the works constructed shall constitute a part of the territory of the country in which they are situated.

Construction of Canal and Channel Facilities: Article VI states that the countries, with the approval of the Commission, may construct, at any time within their own territories, alternative canal and channel facilities for navigation in the International Rapids Section or in waters connecting the Great Lakes. Either country would have the right to utilize such water as is necessary for the operation of such works.

Article VII

Navigation Effect on Neutrality: This Article pertains to navigation on the St. Lawrence and Great Lakes system. It states that the entire Great Lakes system and the St. Lawrence River, including all existing or projected canals, shall be continually open to vessels and citizens of the United States and the British Empire.

Essential portions of the proposed seaway lie either wholly within Canada or wholly within the United States. If the seaway were ever to be used during times of war, when one of the two countries was a belligerent and the other a neutral, it is conceivable that many subjects of dispute would arise. Neither country would have sole jurisdiction over the waterway's use throughout its entire length. Various conditions imposed upon its use would interfere with established trade routes and would cause discord between the two nations.

The seaway would not be invulnerable to attack or sabotage. Its entire effectiveness could be nullified by a single act of sabotage. Further, which country would defend it in case of attack? This is a question which becomes especially acute when one of the countries is at war and the other at peace.

Serious questions have been raised in various quarters as to whether the entering into such a treaty with Canada, a belligerent nation, does not constitute a complete violation of the spirit of United States neutrality. Many critics of the St. Lawrence project have pointed out that the United States, if the St. Lawrence plan were realized, would be aiding a belligerent country to improve its war-time and national defense efforts for some future war if not for the present one. This attitude is prompted by the fact that Canada would use the proposed St. Lawrence hydro-electric power developments to stimulate industries which would be capable of producing war materials.

The United States now has thousands of miles of seacoast, so it seems unwarranted to expend hundreds of millions of dollars in developing an outlet to the sea through a foreign country.

United States Sovereignty over Lake Michigan: It is stated in Article VII that nothing in the treaty shall be construed as infringing or impairing the sovereignty of the United States over Lake Michigan.

The undoubted reason for the inclusion of this section is that no such provision appeared in the previous treaty (1932). When the 1932 document was being considered by the United States Senate, there was considerable discussion as to whether the United States, by the terms of that treaty, was not surrendering its sovereignty over Lake Michigan, a body of water lying entirely within the United States.

The writing of this declaration into the proposed 1938 treaty, however, does not wholly protect the rights of the United States in its sovereignty over the waters of that lake, for a definite limitation has been placed upon the use of these waters in the subsequent Article (VIII).

This Article limits the amount of water which may be withdrawn from Lake Michigan at Chicago for the sanitary requirements of that city and the further development of the Great Lakes-Mississippi Valley-Gulf of Mexico waterway. The United States has no existing treaty with Canada which in any way would interfere with the development of such a canal. By writing such a provision into the proposed treaty, the United States surrenders her right to develop a deeper waterway from Chicago to the Gulf if at any time she should deem it to her best interest to do so.

Article VIII

Further Remarks on the Sovereignty over Lake Michigan: In 1848, a waterway paralleling the Des Plaines and Illinois rivers was opened between Lake Michigan, at Chicago, and the Mississippi River. At that time water was withdrawn for navigation needs only. Subsequently, improvements to the canal were made and additional water withdrawn for sanitary purposes. This waterway serves a triple purpose: to drain and dilute Chicago sewage; to carry traffic between the Great Lakes and the Mississippi Valley through to the Gulf ports; to generate hydro-electric power.

In the past, a maximum of 10,000 cubic feet of water per second has been permitted to be withdrawn from Lake Michigan for these uses. But in 1931 the United States Supreme Court, as a result of litigation between various states, ordered this water withdrawal limited to 1500 c.f.s., plus certain pumpage. It is quite possible that, upon review of the situation, the United States Supreme Court might modify its ruling. Under the terms of the proposed 1938 treaty, however—and a treaty is the lighest law of the land—the amount would be definitely limited, except in the case of emergency, to 1500 c.f.s. This restriction could not be changed except with the consent of a foreign country, Canada. Such a condition makes for a definite surrender of the sovereign rights of the United States.

Under this treaty section, the question of any further diversion at Chicago to meet any emergency must be submitted to an international tribunal, if Canada should object to the added withdrawal. The tribunal would be composed of one Canadian, one citizen of the United States and a chairman appointed by both countries.

This treaty places in the hands of a foreign country the fate of the future development of a Great Lakes-Gulf of Mexico waterway.

Compensatory and Regulatory Works: Article VIII also directs the Commission to undertake a study of compensatory and regulatory works in the Great Lakes System. This means that they are to study and prepare plans and cost estimates for dams, weirs, gates and other works necessary to control the levels of Lakes Michigan, Huron, Erie and Ontario.

Endless volumes could be written upon the magnitude of this regulatory problem. Similar work has been undertaken for control of Lake Superior. It operates with success insofar as that particular lake is concerned but has an adverse effect upon the lower lakes. In the event works were arranged to regulate the flows from all of the lakes, the ramifications of the project would be tremendous. The first cost would be great, and the operation itself would require infinite finesse to prevent serious international complications.

Canadian ports along the St. Lawrence must be assured that harbor levels would not be affected by various works in the Great Lakes or in the portions of the river up-stream from the ports. The Montreal Chambre de Commerce, in a recent resolution, declared that if a treaty were signed by the United States and Canada, a provision should be included to remedy the lowering of water in the Montreal harbor. It is obvious, as demonstrated by this resolution, that Montreal demands guarantees protecting her port. This is an indication of the potential perils of an undertaking which, if incorrectly handled, would bring prompt protest from Canada and thus threaten the international amity.

Article IX

Niagara Falls: In this Article, an inducement is offered to previous opponents of the St. Lawrence Seaway Project. This is in the form of an agreement to consider the preservation and restoration of the beauty of Niagara Falls and the development of additional power at the Falls. For years the Province of Ontario and the State of New York have fought for this project. It has long been recognized by Ontario and the State of New York that the scenic beauty of the Falls has been seriously impaired by excessive erosion.

Appointment of Special International Board: As a result of preliminary investigations, a Special International Niagara Board in 1927 found that the beauty of Niagara Falls could be restored, erosion reduced to an absolute minimum and some 20,000 cubic second feet of additional water, available for power purposes, could be withdrawn and divided equally between the United States and Canada. Ten thousand cubic feet of water per second at Niagara would be capable of developing 300,000 horsepower. These recommendations never have been adopted. The Niagara Falls Project, like the Long Lake diversion plan, has been made contingent, by the Administration in Washington upon the realization of the St. Lawrence Seaway and Power Project. The Administration apparently has adopted this attitude in the hope that it could induce the Province of Ontario to support the St. Lawrence Seaway Project in return for the Niagara Falls development. There is no technical demand, though, for coupling the St. Lawrence and Niagara Falls projects.

Under Article IX of the proposed treaty, the Commission would proceed with plans for Niagara River works according to the recommendations of the Special International Niagara Board. But the proposed Treaty states that the governments shall not consider the Niagara Falls project until after the adoption of the final plans for the project in the International Rapids Section.

Articles X & XI

Damages and Ratification: These Articles of the proposed Treaty are not particularly controversial. They state that each government is released from responsibility for damages in the other's territory as a result of actions authorized in the proposed Treaty, and that the documeat shall be ratified in accordance with the constitutions of the two countries.

Summary of Proposed Treaty of 1938

Although details on the treaty draft which is now being considered by the two governments are not currently available, it is likely that the new document will closely resemble the proposed instrument of 1938. Thus it is necessary to analyze that earlier paper.

The 1938 draft establishes a Great Lakes-St. Lawrence Basin Commission of not more than ten members with the United States and Canada equally represented. This group would prepare plans for the project in accordance with the Joint Board of Engineers supplemental report of 1927. Construction would be so allocated that each government would build the works in its own country. Since the United States would pay the major portion of cost in the International Rapids Section (under Article III) the result would be the expenditure of United States moneys for Canadian labor and materials there.

Not later than December 31, 1949, Canada must provide for her share of the seaway works, according to the proposed treaty. Whether Canada, now at war, would be in a position at that time to assume the heavy fiscal obligations is a moot point. Obviously, if she were not, the United States properly might become concerned over having spent vast sums for a project which would be worthless as a navigation route.

Under Article III, the United States agrees to pay for all the International Rapids Section development, except power house superstructures, rehabilitation works, side canals and locks on the Canadian side, and for all interconnecting channels between the Great Lakes above Lake Erie. In other words, this country would completely finance the dams and power house substructures among other works on both sides in the International Rapids Section.

Article VII provides that the Great Lakes and St. Lawrence shall be continually open to vessels and citizens of both countries, but the whole proposed St. Lawrence route could be closed to navigation by a single act of sabotage. During wartime, especially when one nation is a belligerent and the other a neutral, the question arises as to which country would defend the seaway from attack. There is also the matter of a neutral's shipping through a belligerent country. Is it wise for a nation already having thousands of miles of seacoast to seek another outlet through a foreign land?

The proposed treaty guarantees the sovereignty of the United States over Lake Michigan, which lies entirely within the boundaries of the United States, but at the same time the instrument is contradictory because it limits the withdrawal of Lake Michigan water, for use in the Chicago Drainage Canal, to 1500 cubic feet per second. The treaty, therefore, virtually destroys, by freezing this restriction into an international contract, the right of the United States to develop further the Great Lakes-Gulf of Mexico waterway.

Provisions for the restoration and preservation of Niagara Falls beauty and for the coincident withdrawal of more water there for power purposes are contained in the 1938 document. The Niagara Frontier Planning Board long has advocated further development of the Falls, but the proposed treaty unfortunately states that this project cannot proceed until final plans for the International Rapids Section have been made. When the Niagara Falls plan is made contingent on construction of the detrimental St. Lawrence seaway, the latter loses its justification as an improvement of the general welfare.

DESCRIPTION

Existing Waterways in Great Lakes-St. Lawrence River Area — Duluth to Open Ocean via Present St. Lawrence Canals — Chicago to Ocean via Present St. Lawrence Canals — Existing New York State Barge Canal Route — Existing New York State-Oswego Canal Route — Present Chicago-Mississippi River Route — The Navigation Project — Introduction — Purpose of the Project — The St. Lawrence Section — Dams and Locks — The Great Lakes Section — Mileages, Depths and Other Data — Works in the St. Marys River — Works in the Detroit-St. Clair Section — Welland Ship Canal — Deepening of Harbors — Sizes of Proposed Locks and Channels — International Rapids Section — Introduction — The Joint Board Plan — The United States Plan — Spillway — Power Houses — Dykes — Locks — Channels — Control Works — Railway and Highway Relocating — Hazards — Summary.

᠊ ᠊ ᠊

Existing Waterways in Great Lakes—St. Lawrence Area

THERE are several existing waterways which now connect the Great Lakes system with the north Atlantic Ocean. One is the St. Lawrence River and Canals extending from Lake Ontario to the Gulf of St. Lawrence and thence to the Atlantic Ocean. There is also the New York State Barge Canal (often called the Erie Canal, although this is no longer the official title) extending from Buffalo to the Hudson River and thence to New York City and the Atlantic. Another is the New York State-Oswego Canal which connects Lake Ontario with the New York State Barge Canal at Three Rivers. Still another route follows the Canadian Champlain Canal which extends southward from the St. Lawrence River to Lake Champlain, the New York-State Champlain Canal and the Hudson River.

Connecting Lake Michigan with the Mississippi River and through that route with the Gulf of Mexico is the Illinois waterway. It comprises the Chicago Sanitary and Ship Canal, the south branch of the Chicago River, the Des Plaines River and the Illinois River.

Duluth to Open Ocean via Present St. Lawrence Canals: The distance from Duluth to open ocean via the Great Lakes System, the St. Lawrence River and the St. Lawrence Canal, is 2,350 miles. Eleven hundred and sixty four miles lie in the Great Lakes, 183 miles in the St. Lawrence River above Montreal and 1,003 miles in the St. Lawrence River and Gulf of St. Lawrence below Montreal.

The route traverses the open waters of Lakes Superior, Huron, Erie and Ontario. The passage from lake to lake has been made possible by the removal of obstructions in the St. Marys River between Lakes Superior and Huron, and by the construction of locks in that section, by the deepening of channels in the St. Clair River, Lake St. Clair and Detroit River between Lakes Huron and Erie; and by the construction of the Welland Canal between Lakes Erie and Ontario. The St. Lawrence River route above Montreal has a minimum depth of 14 feet. The river section consists of 134 miles of open water and 49 miles of side canals. ccnstructed completely within Canada. The difference of 224 feet between the water level of Lake Ontario and the water level at Montreal is overcome by a series of locks placed in the following canalized sections:

Galop Canal	15½ feet lift	Cornwall Canal	48 feet lift
Rapide Plat Canal	11½ feet lift	Soulanges Canal	84 feet lift
Farran's Point Canal	4½ feet lift	Lachine Canal	45 feet lift

The route from Montreal to the sea is via improved 30 foot channels to Father Point, and thence through the deep open waters of the St. Lawrence River and Gulf of St. Lawrence for the remaining 652 miles.

Chicago to Ocean via Present St. Lawrence Canals: The distance from Chicago to open ocean by way of the existing St. Lawrence canal is 2,249 miles; 1,063 miles lie in the Great Lakes, 183 miles in the St. Lawrence River above Montreal, and 1,003 miles below Montreal.

The route on the Great Lakes traverses the open waters of Lake Michigan and joins the route from Duluth at the northerly end of Lake Huron. From there to open ocean it is the same as described in the preceding paragraphs.

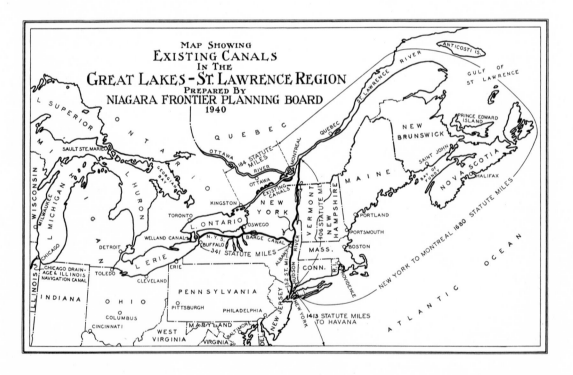

Existing New York State Barge Canal Route: The Barge Canal from Buffalo to Three Rivers has a minimum depth of 12 feet. The minimum bottom width in lakes and canalized rivers is 200 feet, and in canal land routes it is 75 feet. Locks are 300 feet long, 44½ feet wide and have a depth of water over the sills of 12 feet. Clearance under bridges is 15½ feet. From Three Rivers to the Hudson River, the channels are being deepened to 14 feet and clearance under bridges is being increased to 20 feet.

The total distance from Buffalo to the Hudson River is 341 miles. From Waterford, where the Barge Canal meets the Hudson River, it is 155 miles to New York City, making a total of 496 miles from Buffalo to New York. From Chicago and Duluth to Buffalo, the shipping lanes traverse the same routes to the lower end of Lake Erie as were described in the paragraphs relating to the existing St. Lawrence Canal. From Duluth to New York City via the Barge Canal it is 1,482 miles and the distance from Chicago to New York City via the same route is 1,389 miles.

Existing New York State-Oswego Canal Route: An alternate route from the Great Lakes System to New York City and the open ocean is available through use of the Oswego Branch of the Barge Canal. The distance from Oswego to Three Rivers is 23.8 miles. This branch of the Barge Canal system has a depth of 14 feet in the channels and clearance under bridges of 20 feet, the same depth and clearances as exist in the Barge Canal from Three Rivers to the Hudson River.

The total distance from Oswego to New York City by way of the Oswego and Barge Canal is 321 miles. This route is open to Duluth, Chicago and other Great Lakes ports via the same channels and shipping lanes to the easterly end of Lake Ontario as were described in the paragraphs relating to the St. Lawrence Canal. The total distance from Duluth to New York City, by way of this route, is 1,465 miles, and the distance from Chicago to New York, 1,364 miles.

Present Chicago-Mississippi River Route: A connection between Chicago and the Mississippi River is available through the waterway which includes the Chicago Sanitary and Ship Canal, the south branch of the Chicago River, the Des Plaines River and the Illinois River. The distance from Chicago to the mouth of the Illinois River, which meets the Mississippi at a point about 38 miles above St. Louis, is 326 miles. This waterway has a minimum depth of 9 feet with widths ranging between 200 and 300 feet. It includes several locks and dams to make navigation possible.

This 326-mile route between Chicago and the Mississippi River is broken down into the following distances: Chicago Sanitary and Ship Canal and south branch of the Chicago River, 35 miles; Des Plaines River, 18 miles and Illinois River, 273 miles. Through this waterway is established a link to form the Chicago-Mississippi-Gulf of Mexico route.

Other Existing Inland Waterways: The United States Government has also spent large sums upon other inland waterways. These include the Missouri River, the upper Mississippi River, the Ohio River, and the lower Mississippi.

Other Existing Transportation Facilities

In addition to these many water routes, there is a vast network of railroads connecting the interior of the country with all seaboards. These roads can now handle 65% more tonnage than that handled in 1918, a maximum traffic year. Likewise, they are capable of handling 75% more tonnage than was handled in 1929.

There are in addition to the railroads certain other important transportation facilities, such as highways, airways and pipe lines. Since 1920, the capital investment in improved roads, further waterway improvements and in airways has exceeded fourteen billion dollars.

That existing transportation facilities (waterways, railroads and highways) are adequate, dependable and efficient for the entire Great Lakes area which might be served by the seaway is proven by the industrial development of that section. It now comprises 35% of the United States population, produces 38% of all manufactured products, purchases 47% of the raw materials and produces 52% of all the crops. Clearly no such development could have taken place had there been any lack of efficient, dependable and adequate transportation service. No other area in the United States can be said to have developed more rapidly or more completely than this very area.

The Navigation Project

Introduction: The following eight pages describe the St. Lawrence seaway part of the general St. Lawrence Seaway and Power Project. Then are discussed such important elements of the proposed navigation works as costs; as the type of ships expected to use the seaway; as the navigation season; as possible cargo shipments and the effects of such shipments upon existing American transportation port and terminal facilities, closely allied industries and labor. Possible savings in shipments of cargoes over the St. Lawrence seaway are compared with the cost of its maintenance and amortization, operation and losses to American industries.

Purpose of the Project. The purpose of the navigation part of the proposed works is to create a 27-foot navigable channel via the St. Lawrence River from Montreal to Lake Ontario and thence through the entire Great Lakes System by way of the Welland Canal and other connecting lake channels.

The St. Lawrence Section

The St. Lawrence River between Lake Ontario and Montreal is divided into five sections. They are, starting at Lake Ontario and proceeding downstream:

1. The Thousand Islands Section
2. The International Rapids Section
3. The Lake St. Francis Section
4. The Soulanges Section
5. The Lachine Section

The Thousand Islands Section is similar to a large lake dotted with many islands and extends from Lake Ontario proper to Chimney Point, New York, a distance of 67 miles. The International Rapids Section extends 48 miles from Chimney Point to the headwaters of Lake St. Francis. This reach is composed mostly of rapids and swiftly running water. The Lake St. Francis Section is 27 miles in length and has quiescent water most of which is deep enough for the 27-foot channel. The Soulanges channel extends from deep water in Lake St. Francis to Lake St. Louis, a distance of 18 miles. A large portion of this section is composed of swiftly flowing rapids. The Lachine Section extends from Lake St. Louis deepwater to the Montreal harbor, a distance of some 24 miles. Thus the total distance from Lake Ontario to Montreal Harbor is 184 miles.

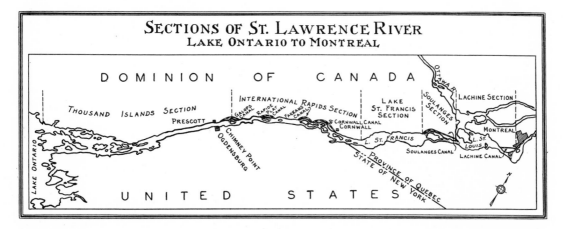

International Section: The International Section includes the Thousand Islands and International Rapids Sections. It forms the boundary line between the Province of Ontario and the State of New York. The remaining sections lie wholly within the Dominion of Canada.

In order to create a navigable channel and overcome the difference in elevation between Lake Ontario and the St. Lawrence River at Massena Point, it is necessary to construct a dam or dams. In the event one dam is constructed for this purpose, the work is called "Single Stage Development." In the event two dams are constructed, one at Barnhart Island and the other at Crysler Island, it is called "Two Stage Development." In the case of single stage development, there would be a dam some 85 feet high located at the foot of Barnhart Island, across the river from Massena point.

Additional dams, one at Beauharnois and another at Lachine, are necessary in that part of the canal located wholly within Canada for control of water levels at those points. Seven or eight locks, depending upon whether single or two stage development is adopted, would be required. The combined total lift through the locks would approximate 219 feet.

In the case of the two stage development, a lock would be required at Crysler Island some 26 feet high and two at Barnhart Island, one with a lift of 14 feet and the other with a lift of 48 feet. In the case of single stage development, a flight lock would be required at Barnhart Island having a lift of some 85 feet. For that section of the canal below the International Rapids Section, one lock of two 39-foot lifts and one guard lock would be required in the Soulanges Section. In the Lachine Section, three locks having lifts of 20 feet, 12 feet and 21 feet, respectively, would be required.

With the exception of the Lachine, Soulanges and short canals around the International Rapids Section, the navigation channel would follow the present stream bed of the St. Lawrence River. Below Montreal the route would traverse present channels of 30-foot depth for a distance of some 351 miles to Father Point. From there on, the route is through 652 miles of open water in the St. Lawrence River and the Gulf of St. Lawrence to the sea.

The Great Lakes Section

In the Great Lakes System, starting at Duluth, the route would traverse Lakes Superior, Huron, Erie and Ontario. To make passage between these lakes possible, it would be necessary to remove obstructions in the St. Marys River between Lakes Superior and Huron, and to build a lock in the St. Marys River. It would be necessary also to remove obstructions from the St. Clair River, from Lake St. Clair and from the Detroit River. The difference in water level between Lake Superior and Lake Ontario would be overcome by a lock in the St. Marys River, having a lift of 20½ feet, and by the Welland Ship Canal, with a total lift of 320½ feet.

Mileages, Depths and Other Data: The following table is taken from the Interdepartmental Report, Senate Document No. 116, 73rd Congress, Second Session, Pages 44 and 45. It summarizes the distances from Chicago and Duluth to the ocean, the minimum depth for navigation purposes, the number of locks and the number of movable bridges.

TABLE II
Summary of Proposed Deep Waterway—Duluth and Chicago to Montreal to Open Ocean

Description	Chicago to open ocean	Chicago to Montreal	Duluth to open ocean	Duluth to Montreal
	miles	miles	miles	miles
Miles of open water—no speed reduction..	2,177	1,174	2,276	1,273
Miles of restricted channels requiring reduction to 8 miles per hour..............	8	8	8	8
Miles of canals requiring further reduction	65	65	67	67
Total distance	2,250	1,247	2,351	1,348
Minimum water depths				
Great Lakes......................	27 feet		27 feet	
St. Lawrence	27 feet		27 feet	
Montreal to open ocean.............	30 feet		30 feet	
No. of locks; St. Marys River (1), Welland Canal (8)*, St. Lawrence River (9) Total......................	17		18	
No. of movable bridges; St. Marys River (1), Welland Canal (20), St. Lawrence River (8)— Total..................	28		29	

*Includes one guard lock.

Works in the St. Marys River: The St. Marys River is 63 miles long and connects the easterly end of Lake Superior with the northerly end of Lake Huron. At St. Marys Falls, the water level drops 20½ feet. It would be necessary to construct a new lock there for the seaway project because the most modern locks at the Falls now have only a minimum depth of 24½ feet.

Channels would also have to be deepened to 27 feet as they are now 25 feet or less. The following table, taken from the previously mentioned report (page 46), summarizes the work to be done in the St. Marys River:

TABLE III

Description	Length of of river (statute miles)	Minimum depth (feet)	Direction of Traffic	Character of Materials
		Excavate to		
Dredge shoals in upper river...	13	27	2-way	Hard and rock
Construct lock and deepen approaches at the Falls........	2	30		Hard and rock
Dredge channels in lower river .	9	27	2-way	Soft, hard, rock
Dredge '' '' '' ''	14	27	1-way (downbound)	Soft, hard, rock
Dredge '' '' '' ''		27	1-way (upbound)	Soft, hard, rock
Dredge shoals in lower river	25	27	2-way	Soft and hard
Total length of river.........	63			

Works in the Detroit-St. Clair Section: The St. Clair River, 40 miles long, Lake St. Clair, 17 miles long, and the Detroit River, 31 miles long, connect the southerly end of Lake Huron with the westerly end of Lake Erie. The total mileage from Lake Huron to Lake Erie is 88 miles. The work to be done in this section includes dredging necessary to assure a 27-foot navigable depth. The following table, taken from Page 47 of the Interdepartmental Report, summarizes the work to be done.

TABLE IV

Description	Length of river (statute miles)	Minimum depth (feet)	Direction of Traffic	Character of Materials
Dredge shoals in St. Clair River	40	27	2-way	Soft and hard
Dredge channel in Lake St. Clair	17	27	2-way	Soft and stiff
Dredge shoals in Detroit River	18	27	2-way	Hard and rock
Dredge ” ” ” ”	8	27	1-way (downbound)	Hard and rock
Dredge ” ” ” ”		27	1-way (upbound)	Hard and rock
Dredge ” ” ” ”	5	27	2-way	Medium

Total length of river...... 88

Welland Ship Canal: The New Welland Ship Canal is 30 miles long and connects Port Colbourne on Lake Erie with Port Weller on Lake Ontario. The channel has a 200-foot bottom width and a minimum depth of 25 feet. There are 7 locks of 46½-foot lift which overcome the difference in elevation between the two lakes.

The locks have been built to permit a 30-foot depth of water over the sills. However, the channels which run through earth and rock have only been excavated to a depth of 25 feet. Therefore, those channels would have to be deepened 2 feet over a 28.6 mile length.

Deepening of Harbors: While the deepening and widening of the interconnecting Great Lakes channels would be the least expensive part of this whole St. Lawrence project, no major port along the Great Lakes has harbor facilities adequate to accommodate the larger ocean vessels. The harbor at Buffalo, for instance, the largest milling center of the world, is only 22 feet deep. All of these ports would have to be deepened at heavy expense.

Sizes of Proposed Locks and Channels: All locks are to be 859 feet long, with 766 feet between breastwall and fender, 80 feet wide and have a depth of 30 feet of water over the sills.

With the exception of canal sections, channels for navigation have been planned for a minimum width of 450 feet, and wider where desirable on account of bends or currents.

International Rapids Section

Introduction: The major portion of the United States cost would be in the development of the International Rapids Section, which generally is considered as extending 48 miles from Chimney Point to the place where the St. Lawrence River leaves the northerly boundary of New York State, opposite St. Regis. The river drops in this section approximately 92 feet. One-third of this fall occurs in the first 18 miles above Ogden Island; the remaining two-thirds of the fall is below that point.

Present navigation in this section is carried through the existing 14-foot Canadian canals, paralleling the river on the Canadian shore. In order to make this section of the river navigable for deeper draft vessels it would be necessary to construct one large dam (single stage development) so as to create a pool approximately at the level of Lake Ontario and extending from the dam to the Thousand Islands Section. By this arrangement the fall of the river is concentrated at one point, where it can be converted into hydro-electric energy.

The Joint Board Plan

In 1926, the Joint Board of Engineers established two preferred ways of developing the single stage plan. One was by constructing the main dam from the westerly end of Barnhart Island in an arc to the foot of Long Sault Island and from there to the main United States shore. The power dam would be located at the lower end of Barnhart Island and extend in a northerly direction across the narrower branch of the St. Lawrence River and the international boundary line to the Canadian shore. If this plan were used, the approach to the power houses would be through the channels lying between Barnhart and Sheek Islands.

The United States Plan

The United States representatives on the Joint Board of Engineers preferred a different plan. They recommended that a combined dam and power house structure be located at the foot of Barnhart Island and extend in a southeasterly direction to the United States shore. Such an arrangement would be conducive of better flow control because the dam, power house and sluice gates would all be in one structure, these engineers declared. They further stated that, inasmuch as the channel of approach would be wide and most assuredly covered with an ice sheet in winter, various ice complications would be less likely to occur. They further pointed out that the canal necessary to carry navigation around the dam would be approximately one-half the length of the one needed if the main dam were located at the head of Barnhart Island.

The following paragraphs describe the plan recommended by the United States membership of the Joint Board. Should this not be the plan actually adopted in the new treaty, the fundamental essentials would still apply.

Spillway: Large gates have been proposed by the Joint Board of Engineers to control the river flow. Approximately 46 of these sluice gates would be required, each 50 feet in width and 25½ feet in height. These gates are necessary to control the flow of water so as to maintain navigation depths in the St. Lawrence below the International Rapids Section. For instance, when the water wheels are not using a sufficient quantity of water to maintain proper depths in the St. Lawrence below the dam, then the sluices would have to be opened to allow the proper quantity of water to go downstream and thereby make up deficiencies of the generating units. Contrariwise, when the water wheels are discharging great quantities, then many of the sluice gates would probably be closed. The regulation of these gates depends not only upon the amount of water which the turbines are taking, but also upon the flow of the St. Lawrence River.

The problem of regulating water levels is especially acute in relation to the Montreal harbor. A drop in the harbor level of course would be disastrous for Montreal, and extreme engineering skill would have to be employed if the power plant and dam operations were not to interfere with the ports downstream. One difficulty to be surmounted is the maintenance of an adequate flow during construction. But even after the project was finished, the dam sluice gates and the flow through the hydro-electric generating machines would have to be managed with enormous adeptness.

Quite rightly, Montreal demands definite guarantees that her harbor would not suffer from the upstream works. Any subsequent interference with the flow, if it were not properly handled, would adversely affect Montreal and perhaps lead to international discord.

Power Houses: Two power houses are proposed, one on either side of the power dam. They are designed to house 22 main units of 54,400 horsepower each at a full head of 85 feet. In addition, each power house would be of sufficient capacity to house three auxiliary units. At the winter head, which, according to the Joint Board of Engineers, would be 75 feet, the capacity of each unit would be approximately 45,000 horsepower.

Dykes: Inasmuch as the levels of the pool to be created by the dam would vary between elevations 240 and 244, in the summer, depending upon the level of Lake Ontario, it would be necessary to construct a series of dykes more or less parallel to the shore on either side of the river in order to prevent flooding of valuable lands. In fact, if this were not done, complete towns on the Canadian side would be inundated. These dykes would be of the earthfill type. New drainage systems in back of them would be required to reverse the natural flow of surface drainage. In some instances storm water pumps might be required.

Locks: A canal and locks would be necessary for the shipway in order to raise and lower vessels from the present river level to the pond which would be created in back of the main dam. The upper end of the canal would be located on the United States side of the river and extend from a point near Robinson's Bay (or the center of Long Sault Island) to the lower river near Cornwall. Two locks would be required in this canal. In addition to this side canal, a new lock of 14-foot draft would be necessary to maintain navigation over the present 14-foot canal.

Channels: Free open channels for navigation would be provided through-out the entire International Rapids Section with the exception of the side canal and locks previously mentioned. These channels would have a depth of 27 feet. Channel enlargements between Lotus Island and Morrisburg would give a 95,000-square-foot cross-sectional area under ordinary operating levels.

Control Works: In order to control flow of water through the Galop Island channels and to regulate the level of Lake Ontario, a series of sluice gates located between piers would be provided in the north and south Galop Island channels. The gates are proposed to be 50 feet in width with sills conforming generally to the rock surfaces which cross the river at those points. Between the sluice gates, however, would be a clear opening of some 500 feet for navigation purposes with sills at elevation 215.

Railway and Highway Relocating: Because of the pool which would be created above the main dam, it would be necessary to relocate highways and railways on both the American and Canadian shores.

Hazards: When one considers that the flow of the river often varies between 180,000 and 270,000 cubic feet of water per second (81,000,000 gallons per minute to 122,000,000 per minute) and that it is necessary to construct dams and spillways in this swiftly flowing water and at the same time maintain normal flows so as not to disturb the harbor depths at Montreal, one can realize the great hazards which would be encountered during construction. These are the factors which must be kept in mind constantly when considering pro-bable estimates of cost.

Summary of Description

The St. Lawrence Seaway and Power Project is capable of separation into two projects, one involving navigation and the other power. It is the navi-gation portion of the development with which this discussion primarily is concerned at the moment.

The purpose of the navigation project is to open the Great Lakes to ocean-going ships which could use a fresh waterway having a minimum depth of 27 feet. To accomplish this, certain work must be done between Montreal and Lake Ontario and in the links connecting Lakes Ontario, Erie, Huron and Superior.

Thirty-foot-deep channels now exist in the St. Lawrence between Montreal and the Atlantic Ocean. From Montreal to Lake Ontario is a series of 14-foot-deep canals, channels and locks, all of them wholly within Canada. This part of the St. Lawrence is in five sections which, starting at Montreal, may be listed as the Lachine Rapids, the Soulanges Rapids, Lake St. Francis, the International Rapids and the Thousand Islands, where the river meets Lake Ontario. There is a rise of 224 feet from the level of the river at Montreal to the lake. Various dams as well as new canals, channels and locks would have to be built in this Montreal-Lake Ontario sector of 184 miles. It is in the International Rapids Section that a joint power development would be undertaken by the United States and Canada, but this plan for creation of hydro-electric energy could be realized without the building of additional navigation works.

The next piece of construction would be in the 30-mile-long Welland Canal between Lake Ontario and Lake Erie. Locks in this link are currently deep enough, but channels would have to be excavated another two feet.

Extending between Lake Erie and Lake Huron are the Detroit River, Lake St. Clair and the St. Clair River. Various obstructions would have to be removed from that interconnecting waterway, which of course is now navigable for present Great Lakes vessels. In the St. Marys River between Lake Huron and Lake Superior, which also is open to Great Lakes shipping, further obstructions would have to be eliminated and locks would have to be constructed to accommodate deeper-draft ships. No work would be required between Lakes Michigan and Huron.

It would be necessary to dredge all of the major Great Lakes ports for the handling of ocean vessels.

Other present waterways in the Great Lakes-St. Lawrence area (see map on page 18) include the New York State Barge Canal connecting Lake Erie, at Buffalo, with the Hudson River; the Oswego branch of that canal, which runs from Oswego, N. Y., on Lake Ontario, to the main Barge Canal at Three Rivers; the route following the Canadian Champlain canal running southerly from the St. Lawrence River to Lake Champlain, the New York State Champlain Canal and the Hudson River; the Illinois waterway, comprising the Chicago Sanitary and Ship Canal, and the Chicago, Des Plaines and Illinois Rivers to make a route between Lake Michigan and the Mississippi River for an outlet to the Gulf of Mexico.

From Duluth, at the western extremity of the Great Lakes, to the open ocean via the St. Lawrence River is 2351 miles, a distance almost 1000 miles further than from New York City to Havana, Cuba. Duluth to open ocean via the New York State Barge Canal, the Hudson River and New York City is only 1482 miles.

COST ESTIMATES

*Costs by Items of Work — Additional Necessary Allowances — Harbor Improve-
ments — Allowances for Contingencies — Interest During Construction — Amounts
Already Expended — Contribution of the Power Authority of the State of New
York — Probable Total Cost Without Necessary Allowances — Probable Total
Cost with Necessary Allowances — Probable Full Minimum Cost to Both Countries — Segregated Costs of International Rapids Section — Immediate Obligations
in International Rapids Section Based on Deferred Power Development — Immediate Obligations in International Rapids Section Based on Power Develop-
ment on New York State Side and Deferred Canadian Power Development —
Geographic Break-up of Costs — Non-benefiting Area Pays 85% of Cost —
Summary.*

᠊ ᠊ ᠊

Costs by Items of Work

THE following table is an itemization of costs of the single stage (or single dam) development plan recommended by the Joint Board of Engineers in their report of November 16, 1926. Should the design be changed to another single stage development the individual items under the sub-headings would change to some extent. However, the principle involved and approximate amounts shown under the sub-headings would be maintained.

The table shows the cost to the United States and to Canada and the total for the entire project from Lake Superior to Montreal. Some of the work has already been done in the interconnecting channels of the Great Lakes. This amount of work has not been shown in the following table but is taken into account in subsequent tables.

It will be noted that the United States cost in the interconnecting channels is $65,100,000 and that the estimated cost in the International Rapids Section is $185,703,000, giving a total of $250,803,000.

The Canadian cost is $1,100,000 for the work in the interconnecting channels, which item is specifically for deepening of the Welland Canal from 25 to 27 feet. The locks in the Welland are already of sufficient depth to care for the deeper draft. The work in the International Rapids Section amounts to $50,140,000, which item includes $32,140,000 for Canadian power house super-structures, machinery, and rail connections to power houses. In other words, if the Province of Ontario did not wish to proceed at this time with the power development, it would only have to expend $18,000,000 as against a $157,-307,000 expenditure by the United States after the power house superstructures and rail connection items on the United States side have been deleted.

The table also shows that below the International Rapids Section, Canada would have to expend $124,714,000 to complete the navigation project, or a total of $175,954,000 as against $250,803,000 on the part of the United States. The total cost of the project, as estimated by the Joint Board of Engineers, with power development only in the International Rapids Section, is shown in this table as $426,757,000 (necessary additions shown in subsequent tables).

TABLE V

COST ESTIMATES BY JOINT BOARD OF ENGINEERS—NOVEMBER 16, 1926

ITEMS OF WORK	UNITED STATES COST		CANADIAN COST		BOTH COUNTRIES
	Amount	Total	Amount	Total	TOTAL
COMPENSATING WORKS					
Niagara and St. Clair Rivers	$ 3,700,000				
CHANNEL EXCAVATION					
Lake Erie to Lake Superior	54,900,000				
New Welland Canal....................			$ 1,100,000		
ST. MARY'S RIVER LOCK	6,500,000				
THOUSAND ISLANDS SECTION	completed		completed		
Subtotal		$ 65,100,000		$ 1,100,000	$ 66,200,000
INTERNATIONAL RAPIDS SECTION					
Dam—Foot of Barnhart Island..........	$ 18,598,000				
Power House Substructure (U.S.).......	14,452,000				
Power House Substructure (Can.).......	12,548,000				
Unwatering Dams and Power House ..	14,680,000				
Abutments to Power House (U.S.)	1,619,000				
Abutments to Power House (Can.).......	704,000				
Tail Race Excavations (U.S.)............	2,178,000				
Tail Race Excavations (Can.)	2,096,000				
Rail Connections to Power House (U.S.)..	36,000				
Rail Connections to Power House (Can.)..			233,000		
Superstructures power (U.S.)...........	28,360,000				
Superstructures power (Can.)...........			31,907,000		
Navigation Works	22,159,000				
Dykes (Can.)........................			5,871,000		
Dykes (U.S.)........................	6,800,000				
Drainage (Can.)			1,009,000		
Drainage (U.S.)	131,000				
Protection of Iroquois (Can.)...........			1,135,000		
Protection of Morrisburg (Can.)			551,000		
Storm Water Pumps (Aultsville and Farran Point) (Can.)....................			73,000		
14' lock at Bergen Lake (Can.)			998,000		
Control Works, Massena Canal (U.S.)....	2,328,000				
Initial Channel Excavation (U.S.)........	30,072,000				
Channel enlargement to 95,000 sq. ft. section (U.S.)	12,783,000				
Enlargements at Cornwall Island (U.S.)	4,870,000				
Control dam at Galop (for 27' channel) ..	4,787,000				
Flowage damage (Can.).................			6,293,000		
Flowage damage (U.S.).................	4,951,000				
Railroad relocation (U.S.)..............	268,000				
Railroad relocation (Can.)			697,000		
Highway relocation (U.S.)	631,000				
Highway relocation (Can.)..............			1,373,000		
Clearing	652,000				
Subtotal.........................		$185,703,000		$ 50,140,000	$235,843,000
LAKE ST. FRANCIS SECTION.........			1,330,000	1,330,000	1,330,000
SOULANGES SECTION					
Works for navigation..................			32,859,000		
Works common to navigation and power..			34,686,000		
Works primarily for power (37,665,000) not in total					
Subtotal.........................				67,545,000	67,545,000
LACHINE SECTION			55,839,000	55,839,000	55,839,000
GRAND TOTAL..................		$250,803,000		$175,954,000	$426,757,000

DOCUMENTARY REFERENCES

The following are the documentary sources of the various items of estimate:

International Rapids Section—pp. 12, 13, Table 1, Appendix C, Appendices of Joint Board of Engineers Report of 1926.

Interconnecting Lake Channels—p. 19, Joint Board of Engineers Report of 1926 (Government Printing Office, 1927).

Welland Canal Deepening—p. 19, Joint Board of Engineers Report of 1926 (Government Printing Office, 1927).

Lake St. Francis—Table 18, Items a and c, Appendix C, Appendices, Joint Board of Engineers Report of 1926.

Soulanges—Table 10 (First stage and additional cost for navigation channels made 27 feet deep), Appendix C, Appendices of Joint Board of Engineers Report of 1926.

Lachine—Table 31, Appendix C, Appendices of Joint Board of Engineers Report of 1926.

Additional Necessary Allowances

Harbor Improvements: This table (Table V), which was taken from the Report of the Joint Board of Engineers dated 1926, omits several important items of cost which should have been included. One of these items is that of harbor improvements. No major harbor along the Great Lakes is of sufficient depth to accommodate the type of vessel which it is proposed will use the St. Lawrence seaway. The present depths are 25 feet or less, the vast majority of them being less than 22 feet. Senator Wagner, in his minority report of the Senate Foreign Relations Committee, referring to the 1933 Treaty, stated that it would cost at least $25,000,000 per harbor for each of the eight important harbors on the United States side to deepen and accommodate them for the ocean type vessel.

The Brookings Institution, in its St. Lawrence report of 1929, estimated that $25,000,000 would have to be spent on each of ten Great Lakes ports. It was emphasized that this total expenditure of $250,000,000 would meet only "minimum" requirements.

The Engineering Department of the City of Buffalo has estimated that complete improvement of Buffalo's harbor would cost $46,890,000, which sum would cover both private and public expense.

In order to be conservative in this Niagara Frontier Planning Board report, the authors have used a figure of only $7,500,000 per harbor in determining the probable cost of improving the 13 principal ports of the Great Lakes.

Allowances for Contingencies: The Joint Board of Engineers, in its estimates of cost, allowed only 12½% for engineering, legal fees, court costs, administration, contingencies, etc. The cost of these items, other than contingencies, would amount to at least $7\frac{1}{2}\%$. Because that is so, the amount set up for actual contingencies amounts to only 5%. Certainly, in view of the great over-runs of other major canal improvements, a much higher contingency factor should be used, especially when the tremendous construction hazards which were pointed out previously in this report must be overcome.

To illustrate the over-runs occasioned in constructing other canals, it is pointed out that the Chicago Drainage Canal cost $53,000,000 instead of the estimated $16,000,000; the Suez Canal cost $80,000,000 instead of the estimated $30,000,000; the Welland Canal cost $128,000,000 instead of the estimated $114,000,000; and the Panama Canal cost $375,000,000 instead of the first figure of $160,000,000.

After considering these major discrepancies between estimated costs and actuality, it was deemed advisable to add a further item for contingencies. This was taken as $12\frac{1}{2}\%$, which is a very conservative figure. Thus the total contingency percentage is only $17\frac{1}{2}\%$ (5% plus $12\frac{1}{2}\%$). Most private engineers would not set a contingency allowance at less than 20% for such a hazardous project.

Interest During Construction: Another major omission in the Joint Board of Engineer's Report was interest during construction. Almost every authority agrees that it would take at least eight years to complete the project. This being the case, interest during construction on a project of such magnitude would be a major item. Inasmuch as the full amount would not have to be borrowed at the outset but would be borrowed as the work progresses, the interest during construction would not be equivalent to 3% of the total United States cost for a period of 8 years. For the purposes of this report, it was assumed that the amounts would be borrowed in equal installments over equal periods, in which event the average interest would be equivalent to 3% over a period of 4 years.

Amounts Already Expended: As stated previously in this report, money expended by the United States in improving the interconnecting lake channels subsequent to 1926 had not been taken into account in the table entitled "Cost Estimates by Joint Board of Engineers, November 16, 1926." In the preparation of the following table, however, this factor was taken into consideration.

Estimates taken from the I. D. report of 1934, adjusted to include additional expenditures, 1934-1939, show that approximately $21,620,000 has been spent by the United States in deepening of these lake channels. This sum was deducted in the following table prior to computation of additional costs such as contingencies and interest during construction.

Contribution of the Power Authority of the State of New York: The result of negotiations between the Power Authority of the State of New York and the

United States Engineers indicates that the Power Authority contribution for the International Rapids Section development would be approximately $90,000,000. Therefore, this item was deducted from the United States costs to determine the net to that government.

Probable Total First Cost: The following table lists the locations and items of work or contributions, the corresponding estimated amount for both the United States and the Dominion of Canada, together with their combined amounts. The table shows that the initial cost to the United States, after deducting the contribution of the Power Authority of the State of New York, would be $324,771,000; to Canada, $240,601,000, and the total cost $565,372,000.

TABLE VI

Estimate of Probable Cost—Single Stage Project

Items of Work	United States Costs	Canadian Costs	Total
Compensating Works, Inter-connecting Channels, Welland Canal Deepening and St. Marys River	$ 65,100,000	$ 1,100,000	$ 66,200,000
International Rapids Section	185,703,000	50,140,000	235,843,000
Lake St. Francis Section......................		1,330,000	1,330,000
Soulanges Section............................		67,545,000	67,545,000
Lachine Section..............................		55,839,000	55,839,000
TOTAL..................................	250,803,000	175,954,000	426,757,000
Less Already Expended......................	21,620,000		21,620,000
Subtotal................................	229,183,000	175,954,000	405,137,000
13 United States and 2 Canadian Harbor Improvements at approx. $7,500,000 per harbor	100,000,000	15,000,000	115,000,000
Subtotal including harbors	329,183,000	190,954,000	520,137,000
Allowance for Contingencies—12½%..........	41,148,000	23,869,000	65,017,000
Subtotal................................	370,331,000	214,823,000	585,154,000
Interest during construction at 3% for ⅝ years...	44,440,000	25,778,000	70,218,000
TOTAL COST............................	414,771,000	240,601,000	655,372,000
Less amount to be paid by New York State Power Authority	90,000,000		90,000,000
NET TOTAL TO CANADA AND THE UNITED STATES	$324,771,000	$240,601,000	$565,372,000

Probable Total Cost

The preceding tables (Tables V and VI) do not represent the entire cost of the project to the United States or to Canada as they fail to include interest during the period of bond amortization and expense of operation and maintenance. The amortization interest items should be added for the reason that both the United States and Canada are at present operating on borrowed money to finance large annual deficits in current budgets. If the extra costs of the seaway could be paid for out of current revenues, without adding to or creating a deficit, and if neither country had a national debt toward the payment of which any surplus revenue could be applied, these items could be eliminated.

The following table shows these added costs to both the United States and Canada, together with their combined amounts. Interest during the amortization period is taken at the rate of 3% for the United States bonds and is figured upon bond amortization being made in 50 equal annual installments. The 3% figure has been checked by various banking institutions which concur in the opinion that a long term issue of this type would probably call for that rate.

Canadian interest was figured on the basis of 5% because the same banking institutions believed that a long term Canadian issue would call for at least that amount. Operation and maintenance was taken at $1,000,000 per year for both the United States and Canada. It is believed that this is a very conservative figure, since maintenance and operation of the Erie Canal aggregates approximately $2,000,000 annually and other existing inland waterways have comparable amounts. The Government's Interdepartmental Report (1934) estimates that this item would approximate $600,000 a year for the United States. This figure is believed to be entirely too low.

Probable Minimum Full Cost to Both Countries: The following table summarizes the interest, operation and maintenance items and shows that during the 50-year period, the entire cost to the United States would be $623,221,000, that the entire cost to Canada would be $597,367,000, and that the combined cost for the entire project would be $1,220,588,000.

TABLE VII
Cost of Entire Development to United States and Canada

ITEM	United States	Canada	Total
TOTAL COST (See preceding table)......	$ 324,771,000	$ 240,601,000	$ 565,372,000
Interest at 3% based on amortization of bonds in 50 equal annual installments...	248,450,000		248,450,000
Interest at 5% based on amortization of bonds in 50 equal annual installments...		306,766,000	306,766,000
Subtotal.........................	573,221,000	547,367,000	1,120,588,000
Operation and Maintenance during amortization period—1,000,000 x 50..........	50,000,000		50,000,000
Operation and Maintenance during amortization period—1,000,000 x 50..........		50,000,000	50,000,000
GRAND TOTAL..................	$ 623,221,000	$ 597,367,000	$1,220,588,000

3% interest on 100 million during 50 yrs. amortization—$76.5 million.
5% interest on 100 million during 50 yrs. amortization—$127.5 million.

It must be emphasized that these are rock-bottom figures. Many private engineering firms have set the probable cost at sums ranging between two and three times these figures.

Segregated Costs of International Rapids Section

Inasmuch as the proposed treaty specified that the United States shall pay for all works in the International Rapids Section with the exception of power house superstructures on the Canadian side, rehabilitation works, side canals and acquisition of locks on the Canadian side, and inasmuch as the development of power on the United States side is primarily for New York State, it was deemed advisable to segregate the various items of work under headings entitled, "Works Common to Power and Navigation," "Works Primarily for Power" and "Works Primarily for Navigation."

This segregation was made after careful consideration as to what works would be required regardless of whether the project was developed as a power project or a navigation project. Such works were placed under the heading entitled "Works Common to Power and Navigation." The "Works Primarily for Power" were those items which it was believed applied only to the development of power, and likewise "Works Primarily for Navigation" were those which had no direct bearing on the development of power, such as the side canal and lock necessary for the proposed 27-foot channel. This segregation is shown in the following table:

TABLE VIII
Costs of International Rapids Section—Single Stage Development
(Without allowances for contingencies or interest during construction)

ITEM	UNITED STATES COST		CANADIAN COST		
	Amount	Total	Amount	Total	TOTAL
WORKS COMMON TO POWER AND NAVIGATION					
Dam—Ft. of Barnhart Island	$ 18,598,000				
Unwatering Dams only (U.S. and Can.)	7,340,000				
Dykes (Canadian)			$ 5,871,000		
Dykes (United States).................	6,800,000				
Drainage (Canadian)...................			1,009,000		
Drainage (United States)	131,000				
Protection of Iroquois (Can.)...........			1,135,000		
Protection of Morrisburg (Can.)			551,000		
Storm Water Pumps, Aultsville and Farran Point (Can.)....................			73,000		
14' Lock at Bergen Lake (Can.)			998,000		
Control Works—Massena (U.S.)........	2,328,000				
Flowage Damage (Can.)...............			6,293,000		
Flowage Damage (U.S.)	4,951,000				
Railroad Relocation (U.S.)..............	268,000				
Railroad Relocation (Can.).............			697,000		
Highway Relocation (U.S.).............	631,000				
Highway Relocation (Can.)			1,373,000		
Clearing (U.S. and Can.)	652,000				
Initial Channel Excavation.............	30,072,000				
Channel Enlargement	12,783,000				
Enlargement at Cornwall	4,870,000				
Subtotal........................		$ 89,424,000		$ 18,000,000	$107,424,000

(Continued on following Page)

TABLE VIII (*Continued*)

	UNITED STATES Cost		CANADIAN Cost		
	Amount	Total	Amount	Total	TOTAL
WORKS PRIMARILY FOR POWER					
Unwatering Power Substructures........	$ 7,340,000				
Power House Substructure (U.S.)........	14,452,000				
Power House Substructure (Can.)	12,548,000				
Abutments for Power House (U.S.)......	1,619,000				
Abutments for Power House (Can.)......	704,000				
Tail Race Excavations (U.S.)	2,178,000				
Tail Race Excavations (Can.)...........	2,096,000				
Rail Connections to Power House (U.S.)..	36,000				
Rail Connections Power House (Can.)...			$ 233,000		
Superstructures Power (U.S.)	28,360,000				
Superstructures Power (Can.)...........			31,907,000		
Control Dam at Galop (U.S.)...........	4,787,000				
Subtotal...........................		$ 74,120,000		$ 32,140,000	$106,260,000
WORKS PRIMARILY FOR NAVIGATION					
Navigation Works	$ 22,159,000				
Subtotal...........................		$ 22,159,000			$ 22,159,000
TOTALS.............................		$185,703,000		$ 50,140,000	$235,843,000

It will be noted in the above table that in the event complete power development were made on both sides of the International Rapids Section, the United States expenditure would be equal to $185,703,000 and the Canadian expenditure would be $50,140,000, or a total of $235,843,000. Of course, in this event, the United States would receive from the Power Authority of the State of New York $90,000,00 so that the immediate net cost to the United States would be $95,703,000.

Immediate Obligations in International Rapids Section Based on Deferred Power Development

It is likely that the Dominion of Canada would be unable to proceed with the completion of the navigation works which lie wholly within that country because of economic conditions which would prevent such great expenditures during or immediately following the war. Therefore, the following table was prepared to show what the cost would be to the United States, in accordance with the terms of the treaty, for the completion of the International Rapids Section only if the power project on neither the Canadian side nor the New York State side were developed.

In this event, the United States would have to pay the full cost because the Power Authority would be unable to contribute its share. The reason for this is that the Power Authority must obtain funds for construction from the sale of bonds based upon contracts for the delivery of St. Lawrence power to private utilities. If there were no power development, it is obvious that the Authority would be unable to obtain such contracts.

TABLE IX
Immediate Obligations in International Rapids Section Based on Deferred Power Development

ITEM	UNITED STATES	CANADA	TOTAL
Works Common to Navigation and Power......	$ 89,424,000	$ 18,000,000	$107,424,000
Works Primarily for Power .... $ 74,120,000			
Less—Tail Race Excavation (U.S.) ..... $ 2,178,000			
Tail Race Excavation (Can.)...... 2,096,000			
Rail Connections to Power			
Houses (U.S.)......... 36,000			
Superstructure Power (U.S.) 28,360,000			
$ 32,670,000	$ 41,450,000		$ 41,450,000
Works Primarily for Navigation........	22,159,000		22,159,000
Subtotals........	$153,033,000	$ 18,000,000	$171,033,000
Contingencies—12½%........	19,129,000	2,250,000	21,379,000
Subtotals........	$172,162,000	$ 20,250,000	$192,412,000
Interest During Construction 12%%			
(3% x 8 yr. construction period ÷ 2).	20,659,000	2,430,000	23,089,000
TOTAL........	$192,821,000	$ 22,680,000	$215,501,000

It may be noted in the above table that should the Canadians be unable to proceed with the canal project lying wholly within that country, and should it be deemed undesirable to develop power on either the Canadian or the New York State side, the first cost to the United States would be $192,821,000 as compared with a Canadian expenditure of $22,680,000.

Immediate Obligations in International Rapids Section Based on Power Development on New York State Side and Deferred Canadian Power Development

It is probable that the Province of Ontario would defer power development at the International Rapids Section until such time as there is a market for that power. As pointed out previously, it also is likely that Canada would be unable to proceed with the navigation project. In that event, funds spent by the United States in the International Rapids Section would be of no value insofar as the navigation project is concerned. Should the New York State Power Authority develop the power, then it would pay the United States some $90,000,000 as its contribution to the International Rapids Section development. Therefore, the cost to the United States would be the total United States cost less the $90,000,000 paid by the Power Authority.

The following table has been prepared to show what the United States cost would be as compared with the Canadian cost in this event. The main difference between this and the preceding table (Table IX) is that the power house superstructures on the United States side and other direct power items are included and the $90,000,000 contribution from the Power Authority of the State of New York is deducted.

TABLE X

*Immediate Obligations of United States and Canada in International Rapids Section Based on
Payment For Power Development on New York State Side and
Deferred Canadian Power Development*

ITEM	UNITED STATES	CANADA	TOTAL
Works Common to Power & Navigation	$ 89,424,000	$ 18,000,000	$107,424,000
Works Primarily for Power...................	74,120,000		74,120,000
Works Primarily for Navigation	22,159,000		22,159,000
Subtotal	185,703,000	18,000,000	203,703,000
Contingencies—12½%	23,213,000	2,250,000	25,463,000
Subtotal	208,916,000	20,250,000	229,166,000
Interest during Construction			
3% x 8 yrs. construction period ÷ 2	25,070,000	2,430,000	27,500,000
Subtotal	$233,986,000	$ 22,680,000	$256,666,000
Less Amount paid by New York State Power Authority........................	90,000,000		
TOTAL	$143,986,000		

The above table shows that, in the event power is developed on the New York State side and Canada is unable to proceed with the canalization of the St. Lawrence below the International Rapids Section, the United States would be called upon to appropriate the sum of $143,986,000 as against a Canadian cost of $22,680,000.

Geographic Break-up of Costs

In 1934, the United States Government issued an Interdepartmental Report after conducting an economic survey of the proposed St. Lawrence seaway. This document sets up what it calls a tributary area in this country. Embracing states or portions of states which the government believes would be directly affected by trade through the deepened waterway, the territory covers a rough semicircle around the Great Lakes. Thus, the country is divided into two districts, tributary and non-tributary, with the non-tributary sector comprising that approximate portion of the United States which could not benefit from the St. Lawrence project, even if the government's division were accepted without questioning.

The Niagara Frontier Planning Board, as subsequently explained, believes that the government's estimates on transportation cost savings, which would accrue from the seaway, are too high. The scope of the tributary area is directly dependent upon the amount of savings.

When the savings are found to be exaggerated, therefore, the expanse of the tributary area is also found to be too great. But for the sake of conservatism in showing how large a portion of the federal government's cost in constructing the seaway would be borne by the non-tributary section of the country (or in other words, the non-benefiting section), the Niagara Frontier Planning Board uses the area circumscribed by the Interdepartmental Report. Of course, the expense of building the seaway would be a federal taxpayer's charge and consequently would be spread throughout the entire country.

By using other government figures which demonstrate what proportion of taxes come from each state, it is learned that the taxpayers of these non-tributary states, who cannot benefit from the seaway, would pay 64% of the expense of the project.

The following commonwealths, with a total tax contribution of 36% of the aggregate federal collection, are wholly in the non-tributary area:

Maine	New Jersey	Tennessee	Missouri	Arizona
New Hampshire	Delaware	North Carolina	Louisiana	Utah
Vermont	Maryland	South Carolina	Arkansas	Nevada
Massachusetts	Virginia	Georgia	Texas	California
Rhode Island	West Virginia	Florida	Oklahoma	Idaho
Connecticut	Kentucky	Alabama	New Mexico	Oregon
		Washington		

To these must be added the following states, but in each instance the percentage is adjusted because only parts of these commonwealths are in the non-tributary district. With each state is shown the portion which is in the non-tributary classification. They are: New York (80%), Pennsylvania (70%), Ohio (20%), Missouri (30%), Colorado (70%), Wyoming (40%), Montana (20%). The total annual federal tax contribution from residents who are in the non-tributary portion of these states is 28% of the total collection. When the 28% and 36% are added, the figure of 64% results.

It will be noted that the state of Illinois is omitted from the above list. That is because Illinois is considered by the government to be wholly tributary to the proposed St. Lawrence development. It is also noted that portions of New York, Pennsylvania and Ohio are placed in the tributary area by the Interdepartmental Report. As a matter of fact, the losses, which these states would suffer in the diversion of trade away from them, actually warrant the inclusion of the whole of these states in the non-tributary area, because the listing of non-tributary states is virtually a designation of states which could not possibly benefit from the St. Lawrence Project.

Far from being benefited by the St. Lawrence project, as the government claims for the tributary section, these four commonwealths assuredly would be damaged because of the nature of their commercial and industrial facilities.

Non-Benefiting Area Pays 85% of Cost: An anaylsis of this Interdepartmental Report's tributary and non-tributary areas, therefore, shows on the government's own figures that 64% of the cost of the project would be borne by taxpayers who could not benefit from the project, even if the government's claims for the project were to become manifest. When Illinois and the various portions of the other states are added to this percentage the figure exceeds 85%.

Summary of Cost Estimates

Almost unavoidably, estimates of expense for any great project show wide variations. Such is the case in regard to the proposed St. Lawrence development, with private engineers frequently setting figures that double or triple those of government representatives.

The Niagara Frontier Planning Board has selected the most conservative of government estimates for a basis in determining what the absolute minimum cost of the St. Lawrence Seaway and Power Project would be. The experience of other waterway projects in the past, such undertakings as the Suez, Welland, Panama and Chicago Drainage Canals, has shown that the final expense far exceeds the originally planned outlay. There is no reason to believe that the proposed St. Lawrence seaway would not do likewise. The magnitude of the work, costing more than thrice as much as the Panama Canal, would be prone to make the final expenditure soar high above the figures given here.

In 1926, the Joint Board of Engineers set the probable outlay at $426,-757,000, of which the United States would pay $250,803,000 and Canada $175,954,000. Although these totals form the foundation of the Niagara Frontier Planning Board's aggregate estimate, they are entirely inadequate. They include no item for the necessary improvement of Great Lakes harbors, for interest during construction, for interest on amortization or for operation and maintenance. Nor do they cover a sufficiently large contingency percentage, inasmuch as they provide only some 5% for this necessary allowance.

The intense hazards of the proposed St. Lawrence undertaking, especially in the International Rapids Section where about 100,000,000 gallons of water pass every minute, would prompt most private engineers to allow not less than 20% for contingencies, i.e. probable but unforseen events. The Niagara Frontier Planning Board, however, has set the percentage at only 17½% in accordance with the policy of keeping to minimum estimates.

When these absolutely essential adjustments are made, the United States share becomes $623,221,000; the Canadian share, $597,367,000; the total for both countries, $1,220,588,000. The United States portion given here allows for the reduction of $90,000,000 to be rebated by the New York State Power Authority through bond issuance.

Of the United States expense, 64% (based on the government's Interdepartmental Report of 1934) would be met by taxpayers living in areas which would in no way benefit,but in some instances would actually suffer, from the proposed seaway. This 64% figure, when properly revised to account for some of the losses to established transportation routes and business enterprises, rises to more than 85%.

CONDITIONS OF NAVIGATION

Open and Closed Seasons — Reduction in Season Because of Time for Round-Trip — Comparison of St. Lawrence Mileage with Other Routes — Type of Ships Which Could Use Seaway — Government Data on Vessels — Findings of the Brookings Institution — The Tramp Steamer — Other Navigation Features — Tortuous Channels — Single Channel Difficulties — Insurance Rates — Curtailment of Traffic — Foreign Registry — Present Use of St. Lawrence by American Vessels — Summary.

✓ ✓ ✓

Open and Closed Seasons

THE use of the proposed navigation project, extending through the Great Lakes and the St. Lawrence River, would be definitely restricted because of the limited navigation season. For five months of the year, the St. Lawrence River is ice-bound and the surfaces of the Great Lakes are solidly frozen. The navigation dates during the past five years average as follows:

Great Lakes above the Welland Canal from April 9 to December 18

Welland Canal from April 10 to December 15

St. Lawrence River above Montreal from April 23 to December 6

Reduction in Season Because of Time for Round-Trip: The above dates indicate that the Great Lakes-St. Lawrence Seaway would be open and effective for ocean-going vessels from April 23rd to December 6th, which is approximately 7½ months. Actually, however, the effective time would be considerably less than this because the time should be measured from the first day that ocean-going freighters can enter the canal for shipments up the Great Lakes to the last day they can enter the canal and return to the ocean before the navigation season closes.

In order to determine the time required for the trip from Montreal to Duluth, Chicago and return, the following tables were prepared. These tables list the various sections of the proposed seaway, the lengths of such sections in statute miles, the estimated speeds in the restricted channels, the number of locks and the time in hours to navigate. In open water, where no speed reductions would be required, an average speed of ten nautical miles per hour was used in determining the hours for navigation. The first table relates to the time to navigate from Duluth to Montreal, and the second table from Chicago to Montreal.

TABLE XI
Time to Navigate Proposed Waterway—Duluth to Montreal

Location	DISTANCES IN STATUTE MILES			Total Miles	Number of locks	Time to Navigate: Hours
	Open Water no speed reduction	Restricted channels; Speed reduced to 8 nautical mi. per hr.	Canals; Speed less than 8 nautical mi. per hr.			
Lake Superior; Duluth to St. Marys River ..	383			383		33.3
St. Marys River:						
Head of River to St. Marys Falls Canal ..		13		13	1	1.4
St. Marys Falls Canal			2	2		1.0
St. Marys Falls to Point Detour		48		48		5.2
Lake Huron: Point Detour to St. Clair River	223			223		19.4
St. Clair River.....................	40			40		3.5
Lake St. Clair	17			17		1.5
Detroit River.....................	31			31		2.7
Lake Erie to Welland Ship Canal.........	218			218		18.9
Welland Ship Canal			30	30	8	8.0
Lake Ontario: Welland Ship Canal						
to St. Lawrence	159			159		13.8
Subtotal, Duluth to St. Lawrence River.	1071	61	32	1164	9	108.7
St. Lawrence River: Lake Ontario						
to Chimney Point...................		67		67		7.4
Chimney Point to East Williamsburg		23		23		2.5
East Williamsburg....................			3	3		1.0
" " to Grass River Canal .		9		9		1.0
Grass River Canal....................			7	7		3.3
" " to Colquhoun Island.....			6	6	2	1.0
Lake St. Francis		27		27		2.9
Soulanges-Beauharnois Canal			18	18	3	6.0
Lake St. Louis		15		15		1.6
Lachine Canal			9	9	3	5.0
Subtotal, Lake Ontario to Montreal ...		141	43	184	8	31.7
Totals	1071	202	75	1348	17	140.4
Delays.....................						4.6
TOTAL—Duluth to Montreal						145.0

(NOTE: 1 Nautical Mile = 1.1516 Statute Miles)

TABLE XII
Time to Navigate Proposed Waterway—Chicago to Montreal

Location	DISTANCES IN STATUTE MILES			Total Miles	Number of locks	Time to Navigate Hours
	Open Water no speed reduction	Restricted channels; speed reduced to 8 nautical mi. per hr.	Canals; speed less than 8 nautical mi. per hr.			
Lake Michigan: Chicago to						
Straights of Mackinac	321			321		27.9
Lake Huron: Straights of Mackinac to						
St. Clair River.....................	247			247		21.5
St. Clair River.....................	40			40		3.5

Continued on following page

TABLE XII
Concluded

LOCATION	Open Water	Restricted Channels	Canals	Total Miles	Locks	Time
Detroit River..........................	31			31	.	2.7
Lake St. Clair........................	17			17		1.5
Lake Erie:						
Detroit River to Welland Ship Canal	218			218		18.9
Welland Ship Canal			30	30	8	8.0
Lake Ontario: Welland Canal						
to St. Lawrence River................	159			159		13.8
Subtotal, Chicago to						
St. Lawrence River..............	1033		30	1063	8	97.8
Subtotal, Lake Ontario to Montreal						
See Table XI...................		141	43	184	8	31.7
Totals	1033	141	73	1247	16	129.5
Delays........................						5.5
TOTAL—Chicago to Montreal...........						135.0

(NOTE: 1 Nautical Mile = 1.1516 Statute Miles)

From the foregoing tables (Tables XI and XII), it can be seen that it would take about twelve days to navigate the St. Lawrence and Great Lakes between Duluth and Montreal and return. When to this figure is added two days for loading and unloading in the lakes, and also another two days as a safety factor, at least 16 days would have to be allowed for the round-trip. Therefore, when this figure is taken from the 228 days that the canal would be open to navigation, it is obvious that Great Lakes ports could be served by ocean-going ships using the St. Lawrence River only 58% of the year.

Comparison of St. Lawrence Mileage with Other Routes

Inasmuch as many of the European ports are located farther north than New York City, the shortest route to these northern European ports from the Great Lakes would be via the St. Lawrence River. This is especially true if the ships are routed through the Straits of Belle Isle just north of Newfoundland. The distance between Montreal and Liverpool via that route is 3207 statute miles. However, the Belle Isle route can only be used after June. As a consequence, it is often necessary to go south of Newfoundland, in which case the total mileage is 3377 statute miles. The distance between New York City and Liverpool via the winter route is 3578 statute miles; over the summer route, it is 3707 statute miles. The distance from Duluth to New York City via lake and rail is 1382 statute miles.

The following table summarizes mileages along various routes and gives the time for navigation at an average speed of 10 nautical miles per hour.

TABLE XIII
Mileage, Hours and Days Necessary to Navigate

	MILES (Statute)	MILES (Nautical)	HOURS TO NAVIGATE	DAYS TO NAVIGATE
Buffalo to				
Duluth	986	856	98	4.1
Milwaukee	828	719	81	3.4
Chicago	893	775	86	3.6
Montreal	386	335	57	2.4
Montreal to				
Buffalo	386	335	57	2.4
Cleveland	524	455	68	2.8
Detroit	608	528	77	3.2
Chicago	1247	1083	135	5.6
Duluth	1348	1166	145	6.0
New York City	1680	1459	146	6.0
Liverpool (summer route)	3207	2785	279	11.6
" (winter route)	3377	2933	294	12.3
Havana	2847	2472	248	10.3
Belize	3639	3160	316	13.2
New Orleans	3505	3044	305	12.7
Rio de Janeiro	6168	5356	536	22.3
Singapore	11669	10133	1013	42.2
New York City to				
Liverpool	3707	3219	322	13.4
Havana	1413	1227	123	5.1
Belize	1962	1704	170	7.1
New Orleans	1970	1711	171	7.1
Rio de Janeiro	5493	4770	477	19.9
Singapore	11714	10172	1017	42.2
New Orleans to				
Liverpool	5313	4614	461	19.2
Havana	693	602	60	2.5
Belize	979	850	85	3.1
Rio de Janeiro	5972	5186	519	21.6
Singapore	13210	11471	1147	47.8

Thus the distance from Duluth via the St. Lawrence and the route south of Newfoundland (winter route) to Liverpool is 4725 statute miles, while the distance from Duluth to New York City and then to Liverpool via the winter route is 4960 statute miles. This shows a saving of 235 miles in favor of the St. Lawrence route. If the summer route from Montreal and New York City to Liverpool were used the St. Lawrence route would save 534 miles.

As the ports of destination in Europe move southward, the mileage advantage of the St. Lawrence decreases. There is no saving in mileage to ports along the Mediterranean. Of course, when Caribbean or South American ports are considered, the St. Lawrence is at a great disadvantage. Actually, the sea distance from Montreal to New York City is greater than the distance from New York City to Havana. The distance from Chicago to Rio de Janeiro via the St. Lawrence is 7415 miles, while by the way of New Orleans it is 6895 miles and by the way of rail to New York City and thence to Rio de Janeiro the distance is 6402 miles.

Type of Ships Which Could Use Seaway

When considering what type of ships could navigate the deepened St. Lawrence Seaway, one must recognize the difference between the buoyancy

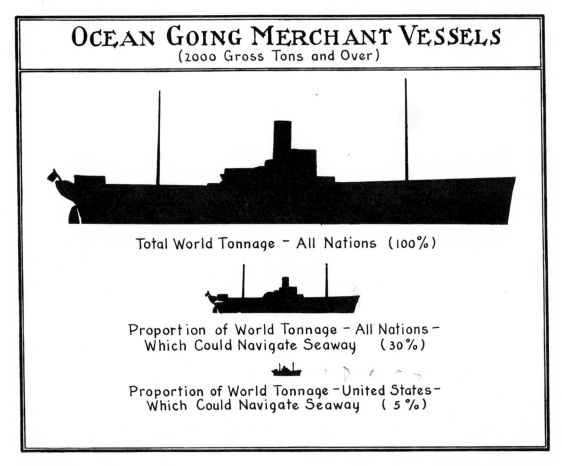

of salt water and of fresh water. Salt water, weighing more than fresh water, will sustain a greater weight for the same displacement volume. A ship of 27-foot draft in the ocean would actually draw 27½ feet in fresh water.

Another factor is the so-called "squat" of a ship in motion. This is caused by sharp turns, by the ship's speed and the effects of currents and winds. In order to secure a sailing permit from Montreal, a ship is required to have a clearance of two feet, six inches. Since the two-foot-six-inch clearance is necessary for safe navigation, a 27-foot channel would accommodate a ship having a fresh water draft of no more than 24½ feet. This is equivalent to a 24-foot draft in salt water.

Government Data on Vessels: In 1932, the records of the United States

Shipping Board indicated that 48% of the registered vessels of over 2000-ton capacity would have a draft of 25 feet or over. These represented 32% of the aggregate tonnage.

The United States Maritime Commission, in its report of December 31, 1937, shows 8,840 registered vessels of 2000 gross tons or over, having a combined tonnage of 49,590,676. Of these, 4,754 have a draft of 25 feet or over; their combined tonnage is 34,568,992. This shows that of all vessels registered in the world in 1937 (2000 gross tons or over), only 46%, representing 30% of the tonnage, could use the St. Lawrence Seaway under full load.

Consequently, it can be seen that, in the five-year interval between 1932 and 1937, the number of ships which could use the St. Lawrence was reduced by 2%, and that the gross tonnage which could use the Seaway also was reduced by 2%. This indicates that the trend in ocean shipping is toward deeper draft boats, and that, as time goes on, the effectiveness of a 27-foot channel in the St. Lawrence seaway would be greatly reduced.

Findings of the Brookings Institution: Through a similar and more extended analysis, the Brookings Institution in 1929 demonstrated that:

1. A 27-foot waterway would be of little use to combination passenger-cargo vessels engaged in United States overseas trade; 85% of these vessels, representing 95% of the aggregate tonnage, could not use such a limited depth waterway.

2. The proposed 27-foot channel could not be navigated by 85% of the faster cargo vessels (12 knots per hour or over), representing 62% of the tonnage now engaged in American overseas trade.

3. The 27-foot channel would exclude 87% of the tonnage operating on a regular schedule out of Montreal and Quebec.

4. The proposed 27-foot seaway would be impossible to navigate by 60% of the aggregate tonnage of grain tramp vessels engaged in overseas Montreal trade.

5. The proposed seaway could not be navigated by 81% of the cargo vessels or any of the tankers engaged in the intercoastal trade.

When considering these findings, one obtains a more critical opinion on the practicability of a 27-foot channel.

The Tramp Steamer: The day of the slow tramp vessel appears to be nearing its end because of the speed-up in business and industry, the ease of communication between countries and the great business enterprises in various countries where there is a necessity for rapid, and scheduled shipments. It is impractical in many instances to rely on the chance of a tramp steamer's happening by with available cargo space for a shipment to a foreign country.

Other Navigation Features

Tortuous Channels: In the proposed waterway there would be many narrow channels abounding in sharp turns. This is especially true in the St. Lawrence River section where many of the channels are cut through solid rock and frequently are completely fog-bound.

Should storms, fogs or adverse cross-currents in these channels require a vessel to anchor, it would be extremely difficult to accomplish such an anchorage safely. To anchor a vessel of even moderate size in many sections of the St. Lawrence River would be dangerous because the ship, swinging at anchor, would be in peril of striking solid rock.

Single Channel Difficulties: In sections along the St. Lawrence where single channels are provided, it would be necessary for vessels to pass. When carriers of any considerable size unexpectedly meet in these channels, a dangerous and difficult situation would result. This condition would frequently arise because there are many sections with insufficient stretches of water ahead to afford enough clear vision to manoeuver the vessels adequately.

Insurance Rates: The aforementioned risk in navigating the various channels probably would be reflected in high insurance rates.

Curtailment of Traffic: The hazards of navigating the dangerous channels and the higher insurance rates would play an important part in reducing the use of the St. Lawrence seaway by the larger tramp vessels. Consultation with many practical navigators has borne out this contention. However, these factors which, in actual practice would materially reduce the amount of tonnage carried over the seaway, have not been considered in the probable tonnage estimates listed subsequently in this report. They have been omitted because it is difficult to determine accurately their exact effect. However, they are important and should not be overlooked when considering the broad aspects of the project.

Foreign Registry: It already has been pointed out that of all the world's registered carriers, only 30% of the aggregate tonnage could use the 27-foot-deep St. Lawrence seaway. Further study of the Maritime Commission Report shows that of this total tonnage, 95% would be in foreign registry.

Present Use of St. Lawrence by American Vessels: The United States Maritime Commission, Department of Research, shows that for the calendar year 1938, the total water-borne foreign commerce of the United States via the St. Lawrence River amounted to 1,926,210 tons. Of this total, 122,876 tons were handled in American ships; 1,660,768 tons in British ships and 142,566 tons in other foreign ships. In other words, only 6% of the United States trade on the St. Lawrence River was handled in American vessels.

This is further evidence that whatever shipping might traverse the St. Lawrence seaway would be preponderantly handled in foreign bottoms, owned by foreign enterprises and operated by foreign labor in direct competition to the American systems of transportation.

Summary of Conditions of Navigation

The annual weather cycle greatly lessens the practicability of the St. Lawrence River as a commercial waterway. Ice keeps the route closed to navigation for five months of the year. Thus whatever savings in transportation costs might accrue could be realized only over a seven-month period. The huge investment in seaway construction would be productive for not more than 58% of the time.

Because of its geographic position, the St. Lawrence route has a mileage advantage over the United States Atlantic Seaboard for shipments to Northern Europe only. No advantage exists in relation to the Mediterranean area, while the St. Lawrence is at a decided disadvantage as far as the Caribbean and South American regions are concerned.

Although it is proposed to deepen the waterway to 27 feet, the maximum draft of ocean-going vessels which might use the seaway is from 24 to 25 feet. Two factors account for this: the difference in the buoyancy of salt water and of fresh water; the necessary allowance for the "squat" of a ship in motion.

Of all the world's vessel tonnage (ships of 2000 gross tons and over), not more than 30% comprises craft having a small enough draft to negotiate the 27-foot-deep channels, canals and locks. Only 5% of the world's tonnage consists of American-owned ships which could use the seaway.

Navigation of the restricted waterway, therefore, would be almost entirely limited to foreign tramp vessels, operating under standards well below those employed on American-owned ships and trading in competition with American systems of transportation.

In addition to seasonal problems, certain other factors must be considered in studying navigation conditions of the St. Lawrence project. The existence of many sharp turns in the narrow channels and the presence of swift cross-currents there would create hazards. These not only would curtail use of the route by mandating extremely slow speeds but probably also would reduce transportation cost savings by calling for high insurance rates.

ANALYSIS OF ESTIMATED SAVINGS

Effect upon Shipping — Possible Cargo Shipments via the St. Lawrence Seaway and Estimated Savings — The Interdepartmental Report — The Fundamental Errors — United States Shipping Board Rates and Rates Constructed in I. D. Report — Bananas — Sugar — Chicago Area — Minneapolis Area — Sugar Competition — Coffee — Kaolin — Grain — Export Movements of Grain — Rubber — Flour and Meal — Export Movements of Flour — Iron and Steel — Agricultural Implements — Automobiles — Packing House Products — Summary.

Effect Upon Shipping

THE opening of the Great Lakes to foreign carriers would mean that American lake, canal and railroad transportation systems would have to meet the competition of foreign labor. These American systems are now gainfully operating with well-organized, well-paid American employees working under high safety and sanitary standards.

Such domestic conditions would be replaced by the lower standards of foreign vessels. Furthermore, the alien seamen's wages, instead of being spent in this country for taxes, household expenses, etc., would be largely distributed in their own home ports.

Possible Cargo Shipments via the St. Lawrence Seaway and Estimated Savings

The savings to American farmers and shippers, which would result from a seaway, depend to a great extent upon its usage by foreign carriers. Enthusiastic prophesies of the volume of tonnage which would use the proposed seaway have been made by various committees and organizations.

Prior to 1934, proponents of the seaway used tonnage estimates formulated in most part by certain private interested organizations. Grossly inaccurate statements were made on the possible savings in shipping various commodities. It was contended, for instance, that economies in shipping wheat from Duluth to Montreal via the St. Lawrence seaway would amount to 8 cents per bushel. The actual cost of shipping this commodity from Duluth to Montreal, however, had only been 6 cents per bushel. Obviously the proponent's estimated saving is incorrect because any transportation saving over present lines of commerce must be made on the Duluth-Montreal section of the route.

The Interdepartmental Report

In 1934, various departments of the United States Government made a report entitled, "Survey of the Great Lakes-St. Lawrence Seaway and Power Project." This has been generally spoken of as the "Interdepartmental Report" and will be referred to hereafter in this discussion as "The I. D. report."

The purpose of this I. D. report was to determine the savings in transportation costs that could be realized by using the proposed St. Lawrence seaway. Ostensibly, the authors of the report wished to show how much cheaper use of the St. Lawrence would be in relation to existing transportation routes. It would have been an interminable task to establish a saving differential for every commodity that might be transported through the St. Lawrence and for each of the multitude of world ports where a commodity might be imported or exported. The Government investigators, therefore, took a list of what they considered to be typical products which might be imported or exported through the St. Lawrence seaway. For each one of these goods they established rates and then compared those rates with costs of existing commercial routes. With these selected commodities as a basis, the authors of the I. D. report then applied an average saving to all other commodities and thereby derived a figure for total savings.

The Niagara Frontier Planning Board has no objection to this type of survey because the Board realizes that it is not practical to make a separate study of every one of the myriad commodities which conceivably could move through the St. Lawrence. But the I. D. report presents findings which were reached through erroneous figures. In other words, the Government's approach to the subject was founded on a proper understanding of method but the method was not fairly applied.

The Fundamental Errors: The I. D. report is faulty on three grounds. First, the estimates of probable tonnages which would be shipped over the St. Lawrence were exaggerated; second, in making comparisons between the St. Lawrence route and existing routes, the cheapest of the existing routes were frequently ignored, and third, the basic rates which were established for the St. Lawrence were out of line with known figures on which they should have been based.

In the following discussion, examples of these three failings are clearly shown. It has been necessary, of course, to revise the findings in this I. D. report because the yardsticks which the report established in determining economies over the proposed seaway are incorrect. The I. D. report's rates, upon which the alleged savings are founded, are so low in many instances that there would be no chance of a shipowner's entering the trade on the St. Lawrence if he had to comply with those figures.

For instance, on page 85 of the I. D. report, the following statement is made: "Furthermore, full loading each way was assumed, a condition that can in reality not be consistently attained." This assertion reveals that the alleged savings are based on two-way loads that cannot exist. The I. D. report admits that it is founded on an impossible hypothesis. But assume that a two-way cargo could be secured for a ship of 24-foot 9-inch draft, with a carrying capacity of 6900 short tons, the type selected by the I. D. report to show the most favorable picture. A full cargo of kaolin (clay) would be loaded at London for Cleveland, where it would be unloaded. The ship then would proceed light to Duluth and there pick up a cargo of grain for Liverpool.

The following figures, based on the rates and costs furnished in the I. D. report, will show that the reported economies are falsely based.

TABLE XIV

EXPENSES

Operating ship—London to Cleveland, loaded, and Cleveland to Duluth, light	$19,728.74*
Operating ship—Duluth to Liverpool, loaded (pg. 90, I. D. report)	19,728.74
Total round trip expense	$39,457.48

EARNINGS

Kaolin (clay)—London to Cleveland, 6900 tons at $1.52 per ton (p. 125)....	$10,488.00
Wheat—Duluth to Liverpool, 6900 tons at $2.80 (pg. 125)	19,320.00
Total freight round trip....................................	$29,808.00
Loss round trip loaded both ways...........................	$ 9,649.48

* Assumed expenses London to Cleveland to Duluth same as expenses from Duluth to Liverpool direct.

The figures used above are based on perfect sailing conditions and no allowance has been made for lost time due to fog, winds, etc., with which steamers must contend, especially in the Gulf of St. Lawrence and west of Montreal. This would add to the loss sustained on the two-way load, "perfect" trip. Consequently, it can be seen that the estimated rates on which the I. D. report bases the stated savings cannot be accepted.

United States Shipping Board Rates and Rates Constructed in I. D. Report: The United States Shipping Board, on request of the Department of Commerce, furnished ocean rates on the commodities studied. These are shown on pages 91 to 99 of the I. D. report. Instead of using these as a basis for computing projected rates to lake ports via the St. Lawrence, the I. D. report constructed theoretical rates for a 24-foot 9-inch draft, 6900 ton freighter. The theoretically constructed figures in the I. D. report are consistently way below the actual rates shown by the United States Shipping Board to and from north Atlantic ports, despite the fact that the distances to the Great Lakes ports are greater and the journey more hazardous.

The big difference between the actual rates and rates constructed in the I. D. report is shown in the following table. This table lists the commodity, the port of shipment and destination, and the rate given by the United States Shipping Board. The fifth column in the table shows the rate as constructed in the I. D. report and the port of destination or origin as the case may be.

TABLE XV

Commodity	From	To	Actual Rate U. S. Shipping Board	I. D. Report's Estimated Rate to Lake Ports
Sugar	Havana	No. Atlantic Ports	$2.10 ton	$1.65 to Chicago, Illinois $1.68 to Duluth, Minnesota
Coffee	Rio de Janeiro	,, ,, ,,	$7.70 ,,	$4.02 to Chicago, Illinois
Clay	Liverpool	,, ,, ,,	$4.20 ,,	$1.52 to Cleveland, Ohio
Rubber	,,	,, ,, ,,	$7.20 ,,	$1.90 to Cleveland, Ohio
Flour & Meal	N. Atlantic	Liverpool	$3.40 ,,	$2.43 from Duluth, Minnesota
Iron & Steel	,,	Rio de Janeiro	$4.00 ,,	$3.63 from Chicago, Illinois
Agricultural Implements	,,	Liverpool	$5.00 ,,	$3.04 from Chicago, Illinois
Autos & Parts	,,	,,	$4.40 ,,	$5.41 from Detroit, Michigan
Packing House Products	,,	,,	$8.00 ,,	$3.04 from Chicago, Illinois

The rates used by the Niagara Frontier Planning Board in calculating possible savings by use of the St. Lawrence are somewhat under those in the above table quoted by the United States Shipping Board. They were obtained from operators dealing in these commodities and represent the cost just prior to outbreak of the present European war. As they are somewhat less than the Shipping Board rates, they reflect to the advantage of the St. Lawrence seaway and their use in this report is in accord with the Planning Board's policy of striving to present a fair picture of actual conditions.

Bananas

In the I. D. report it is stated that substantial movements of bananas from Belize, Central America, to Chicago would be moved over the St. Lawrence. It is stated that during a 12-month period, approximately 740,000 tons would represent the potential shipments to that area. Inasmuch as the canal is open only 58% of the year, this tonnage would of necessity be reduced to an amount equivalent to 740,000 tons times 58% or approximately 429,000 tons. In the I. D. report it is estimated that the savings per ton in shipping bananas from Belize to Chicago via the St. Lawrence would amount to $11.67; that the cost of shipping through the St. Lawrence would equal $5.70 per ton and that the cost of shipping from Belize to Chicago via New Orleans would amount to $17.37. This latter item is broken down into $1.47 per ton, ship costs, and $15.90 rail costs, from New Orleans to Chicago.

There is no question but that the estimated savings and costs of shipping via the St. Lawrence are entirely out of line. It costs approximately $15.00 per ton to ship bananas from Jamaica to Montreal. It takes 280 hours for the trip. Therefore, it can be seen that the cost per ton-hour over that route is $0.0535. By use of this rate in estimating the cost of shipping bananas from Belize to Chicago via the St. Lawrence the cost is determined to be $24.10. This is shown in the following table:

TABLE XVI

| Belize to Montreal | 316 hours |
| Montreal to Chicago | 135 hours |

Total   451 hours at $0.0535 per ton-hour=$24.10

It appears that the rate in the I. D. report from Belize to New Orleans is also too low. The time required for the trip is 85 hours, and at the same rate as used in the above calculations the cost per ton would be $4.55. This, added to the present rail rate of $17.40, shows a through rate of $21.95 by way of New Orleans.

Thus, it can be seen that the cost of shipping this commodity via the St. Lawrence seaway, compared with the existing route through New Orleans, would be approximately $2.15 more per ton. This alone is enough to convince one that bananas will not be shipped via the St. Lawrence seaway.

There is another equally important reason for this, however, and that is the difference in shipping time. The total time by way of New Orleans is only six days while the time via the St. Lawrence would be at least fourteen days. That difference of eight days would represent the difference between fully matured fruit and smaller, less marketable fruit. It would be more desirable to ship over the New Orleans route because of the marketability of the fruit even though the St. Lawrence route were as cheap or even considerably less expensive than the one through the Mississippi Valley.

For these reasons, therefore, this commodity is completely deleted from further consideration as a potential item of St. Lawrence traffic.

Sugar

In the Chicago area, the I. D. report shows an anticipated demand of 630,000 tons of sugar from Havana and 625,000 tons of sugar in the Minneapolis area. This is predicated upon a twelve-month period. The yardstick route in the I. D. report is from Havana to New Orleans and thence up the Mississippi via Federal Barge line.

Chicago Area: The I. D. report's estimated total cost of moving sugar over the Mississippi route to Chicago is $6.73 and over the St. Lawrence route $1.65.

The following analysis will show that these estimates are inaccurate:

The cost of moving sugar from Havana to New York City is $2.00 per ton. The distance from Havana to New York City is 1227 nautical miles; at 10 miles per hour the time for the trip is 123 hours; therefore, the cost per ton hour is equivalent to $0.0163. The distance from Havana to Montreal is 2472 nautical miles; the time consumed in making this trip is 248 hours. Thus, at the above rate per ton hour, the cost per ton movement from Havana to

Montreal would be $4.04. The distance from Montreal to Chicago is 1083 nautical miles. As derived previously in this report, it was shown that 135 hours would be required for the trip. This is equivalent to a cost per ton of $2.20.

The following recapitulates these figures:

TABLE XVII

	per ton
Havana to Montreal 248 hours times $0.0163 (per ton-hour)...	$4.04
Montreal to Chicago 135 " " " " " " ...	2.20
Total	$6.24

It requires 60 hours to make the trip from Havana to New Orleans; therefore, based on the same rate per ton hour for ocean travel, the cost in shipping to New Orleans would be 99 cents per ton. The I. D. report shows that the cost via Federal Barge line up the Mississippi to Chicago is $6.20. In addition, there would be a charge of approximately 30 cents per ton for handling at New Orleans. Therefore, the total cost per ton via this route would be $7.49. Consequently, the saving of shipping sugar via the St. Lawrence route over the New Orleans route would be $7.49 minus $6.24 or $1.25 per ton instead of the $5.08 figure used in the I. D. report.

If sugar is moved by way of the New York State Barge Canal to Chicago, the rate would be as follows:

TABLE XVIII

	per ton
Havana to New York City....................	$2.00
New York City to Chicago (Motor-ship rate) including handling at New York.............	5.00
	$7.00

The economy in shipping through the St. Lawrence route as against the Erie Canal in this instance would be only $0.76 per ton instead of the estimated $5.08 given in the I. D. report. Thus we see that the true saving of the St. Lawrence over the Erie Canal route is 85% below the figure indicated in the I. D. report. Consequently, there should be a considerable reduction in the figures which the I. D. report lists as differentials between rates over the proposed seaway and rates over currently available routes.

The authors of the I. D. survey established an amount of possible tonnage over a St. Lawrence seaway by using as a basis their estimated savings in transportation costs. They assumed that the economies in shipping rates would broaden the market, for goods could be shipped over a wider area and still reach the consumer at current prices. In other words, the differentials in shipping rates would permit the goods to be transported just so much farther without increasing consumers' costs.

For Example: The economies on Chicago imports brought in over the St. Lawrence would be absorbed in transport of those goods by rail from the Chicago dock to the consumer in the hinterlands. The market is extended in proportion to the amount of the saving. The goods could be sold at present prices to consumers who live within the absorption zone.

But when the savings in the I. D. report are found to be too high, this means that the potential market area must also be reduced, because the economies are more quickly absorbed in rail shipments from the docks to the hinterlands. If the I. D. report savings are too high by 85%, the market area is also out of line by 85%. When the market area is properly adjusted, obviously the tonnage estimates must be also adjusted, because the volume of traffic is controlled by the size of the market.

Since the centers of population in the Chicago sector lie close to the city, a full reduction of 85% in tonnage which might use the St. Lawrence would not be completely fair. To be conservative, the authors of this Niagara Frontier Planning Board report have set the reduction at only 35%.

In concluding, the above analysis of sugar transportation shows that there is a possible saving of $0.76 per ton and that the possible twelve-month estimated tonnage required in the Chicago area would be 410,000 tons. This is equivalent to $312,000 instead of the $3,200,400 shown in the I. D. report.

Minneapolis Area: The I. D. report estimates that 625,000 tons of sugar from Havana will be required in the Minneapolis area over a twelve-month period. That report states that the cost of moving this tonnage via the St. Lawrence seaway would be $4.48 per ton and that the cost by way of New Orleans would be $10.53. This is equivalent to a saving of $6.05 a ton.

These figures are also considerably out of line. The rate from Havana to Montreal is $4.04 a ton (as derived in the discussion of sugar delivered to Chicago). It requires 145 hours to run from Montreal to Duluth. This, times the cost-per-ton-hour of $0.0163, is equal to $2.36, and so the estimated total cost per ton from Havana to Duluth would be $6.40. Inasmuch as the St. Lawrence route and the Erie Canal route from Havana to Minneapolis would both pass through Duluth, that port may be considered the terminus for the sake of computing any possible economies. Rail rates between Duluth and Minneapolis would be the same in both instances.

The cost of shipping sugar from Havana to Duluth through the Erie Canal is estimated in the following table:

TABLE XIX

	per ton
Havana to New York City (see Chicago discussion).....	$2.00
Motor ship New York to Duluth including handling at New York................................	5.20
	$7.20

The cost of shipping sugar to Minneapolis via the New Orleans route would be as follows:

TABLE XX

	per ton
Havana to New Orleans (see Chicago discussion)	$0.99
Handling at New Orleans.........................	.30
New Orleans to Minneapolis (via Federal Barge; I. D. Report, page 126)................................	10.00
Total	$11.29

This shows that it is $4.09 more expensive to ship by way of New Orleans to Minneapolis than it would be to ship via Erie Canal to Duluth. Because the rail rate from Duluth to Minneapolis would be less than the $4.09, the cheaper route would be via the Erie Canal. Therefore, this is the existing route which was used in determining estimated savings in shipping over the proposed seaway.

As derived above, the estimated cost of shipping via the St. Lawrence to Duluth is $6.40 per ton, and the cost via the Erie Canal is $7.20. Consequently, the estimated savings would be 80 cents instead of the $6.05 indicated in the I. D. report. This is a reduction of 87% in the savings. As pointed out in the Chicago discussion, this would result in a material reduction in volume. Using a 35% reduction, however, instead of the 87% indicated by the savings, the tonnage on a twelve-month basis required at Minneapolis would be limited to 406,000 tons. This, times the 80-cent savings, would amount to $325,000 in total economy instead of the $3,781,250 shown in the I. D. report.

Sugar Competition: Despite the fact that it appears to be physically possible to make a slight saving in shipping over the proposed seaway to Chicago and Minneapolis, such a saving should not be included in any final computation of St. Lawrence seaway benefits. The reason for this is that Havana sugar would be brought into the very heart of the sugar beet industry area in direct competition with that industry and at rates which are in effect somewhat reduced because of taxation of the sugar beet industry itself. In other words, the beet industry would be taxed for the construction of this seaway and therefore make possible a reduction in sugar rates from Havana to the middle west.

This is contrary to the policy of the United States in reference to the sugar beet industry, which has been encouraged in northern Ohio, Wisconsin, Minnesota, Nebraska, Wyoming, Idaho, and Colorado through various bounties. Furthermore, it has been the foreign policy of the United States to regulate and control foreign sugar importation within positive limits through tariffs and special reciprocal agreements. It is not logical to use possible savings in shipping sugar to the central part of the United States as justification for a seaway expenditure. However, to give the project the benefit of every doubt, the estimated totals directly attributed to sugar are included in the summation of possible economies in shipping costs.

Coffee

The I. D. report estimates that 280,000 tons of coffee would be required in the Chicago area on a twelve-month basis. It further indicates that the cost of moving this commodity through the Port of New Orleans and by Federal Barge to Chicago would amount to $9.78 per ton; that the cost via the St. Lawrence seaway would be $4.02.

It costs 50 cents per bag of 131 pounds to ship coffee from Rio de Janeiro (the port of origin in the I. D. report) to either New Orleans or New York City. It requires 519 hours to make the trip from Rio de Janeiro to New Orleans and 477 hours to New York City.

Using the New Orleans route as a criterion (this would give the least cost per ton-hour), we find the cost of moving coffee per ton-hour would be $7.63 per ton divided by 519 hours, or $0.0147 ($7.63 per ton is equal to 50 cents per 131 pounds). Having the cost per ton-hour, we then can estimate the cost of moving coffee from Rio de Janeiro to Chicago via the St. Lawrence seaway. This is set up in the following table:

TABLE XXI

	per ton
Rio de Janeiro to Montreal, 536 hours x $0.0147	$7.88
Montreal to Chicago, 135 ” x ”	1.98
Total	$9.86

The cost of moving this commodity by way of New Orleans is set up in the following table:

TABLE XXII

	per ton
Rio de Janeiro to New Orleans, 519 hrs. x $0.0147	$7.63
Handling at New Orleans	.30
New Orleans to Chicago (Federal Barge Line)	6.60
Total	$14.53

It would be cheaper to ship coffee through the Erie Canal to Chicago as indicated in the following table:

TABLE XXIII

	per ton
Rio de Janeiro to New York City (same through rate as to New Orleans)	$7.63
New York City to Chicago via motorship, handling in New York included in rate	5.40
Total	$13.03

The I. D. report estimates the saving per ton as $5.76. From the above tables it can be seen that the saving will actually be $13.03 minus $9.86, or $3.17. This reduction of 45% in savings in the I. D. report, as described in paragraphs relating to movement of sugar to Chicago, greatly affects the estimated probable tonnage. However, in order to be conservative, a 20% figure is used in this report. This reduction indicates a possible tonnage of 224,000. This volume, times the estimated saving of $3.17, is equivalent to a saving of $710,000 instead of $1,612,800 as shown in the I. D. report.

While these figures are used in assuming possible savings through the St. Lawrence seaway route, it is not admitted that they will actually accrue. The reason for this is that the roasting and blending of coffee is a specialized trade now mainly concentrated in New York City and New Orleans. After roasting and blending, rapid delivery is necessary. Since the canal would be closed for 42% of the year, it would be necessary to depend upon the New York and New Orleans blending and roasting establishments during that period. As a result, it appears that it would be uneconomical to establish duplicate roasting and blending and distributing establishments in the Chicago area for use during only 58% of the time.

Kaolin

In the I. D. report is it estimated that 140,000 tons of kaolin (clay) would move from Liverpool to Cincinnati via the St. Lawrence route. It is claimed that the savings per ton in using this route over the Philadelphia route via rail to Cincinnati is $1.01.

Investigations of this commodity show that only a small percentage of the imports go through the port of Philadelphia to Cincinnati. This is a clear indication that the demand (small as it is) for this commodity is wide-spread and not just concentrated in the one area (Cincinnati) as implied in the I. D. report. Kaolin is used in the manufacture of paper, rubber, paint, oilcloth and other products which are made in a wide area. It is believed 140,000 tons, which far exceed actual imports, would not be shipped over the St. Lawrence seaway. This is particularly true when one considers that kaolin is produced commercially in Georgia, South Carolina and Pennsylvania and now moves from South Carolina and Georgia to Cincinnati by rail at a rate of $4.28 per ton.

In 1934 and 1935 the United States production was far greater than the imports, as is shown in the following table:

TABLE XXIV

Year	Imports	U. S. Production
1934	100,775 tons	426,335 tons
1935	125,960 "	523,585 "
1937	130,800 "	not available

Furthermore, of the 130,800 tons imported in 1937, only 45,000 tons were imported through Atlantic ports.

The I. D. report constructs a rate of $6.12 via the St. Lawrence seaway and states that the cost of shipping from Liverpool to Cincinnati by way of Philadelphia is $7.13.

The United States Shipping Board advised the Department of Commerce (pages 91-99 I. D. report) that the rate on kaolin from Liverpool to Philadelphia was $4.20 per ton. Since it takes 325 hours for the trip between Liverpool and Philadelphia, the cost per ton-hour over that route would be $0.0129. From this rate it is possible to construct a water rate from Liverpool to Cleveland. This is shown in the following table together with the present rail rate from Cleveland to Cincinnati.

TABLE XXV

		per ton
Liverpool to Montreal	279 hours x $0.0129.....	$3.60
Montreal to Cleveland	68 hours x $0.0129.....	0.88
Cleveland to Cincinnati, rate........................		4.80
	Total	$9.28

The present cost of shipping from Liverpool to Philadelphia and thence by rail to Cincinnati is shown in the following table:

	per ton
Liverpool to Philadelphia	$4.20
Philadelphia to Cincinnati, rail	6.80
Total	$11.00

From the above tables it can be readily determined that any possible saving in shipping this commodity from Liverpool to Cincinnati through the proposed St. Lawrence route would not exceed $1.72 per ton.

Inasmuch as only 45,000 tons of kaolin were imported in 1937 through all of the North Atlantic ports, it was believed that if this amount were assumed to move via the St. Lawrence seaway, it would be a liberal allowance to use in computing the total possible savings. This tonnage, times the estimated economy of $1.72 per ton, is equivalent to a saving of $77,000 per year. This is 45% less than the saving indicated in the I. D. report.

Grain

The I. D. report estimates that 2,618,000 tons of grain, based on a twelve-month period, are available for movement through the proposed St. Lawrence seaway. The yardstick route which is taken in this report is from Duluth to Buffalo and thence by Erie Canal to New York City where it is trans-shipped for the Liverpool market. The I. D. report estimates that the present cost of shipping over the yardstick route is $5.24 per ton, and that over the proposed St. Lawrence route the rate would be $2.80 per ton. Thus it is indicated there would be a saving in shipment of grain equivalent to $2.44 per ton.

The following table shows the cost per year from 1930 to 1938 of grain movements from the head of the lakes to Montreal and Buffalo, and from Montreal to London, New York City to London, and Buffalo to New York City via the Erie Canal.

TABLE XXVI

Freight Charges for Wheat Movement—Cents per Bushel

Year	Head of Lakes to Montreal	Montreal to London	Head of Lakes to Buffalo	Buffalo to New York City via Erie Canal	New York City to London
1930	7.95	4.63	1.91	5.13	4.53
1931	6.46	5.70	1.71	3.51	4.66
1932	5.09	5.06	1.43	3.50	4.50
1933	3.71	4.50	1.60	2.50	4.50
1934	5.81	5.00	1.74	3.50	4.50
1935	4.49	5.49	1.87	2.16	5.13
1936	4.40	6.86	1.99	2.19	7.07
1937	3.96	10.31	2.18	2.57	9.19
1938	5.57	8.35	2.23	3.52	8.21
Average	5.27	6.21	1.85	3.18	5.81

By using the average costs shown above, it is possible to determine the average cost of shipping wheat to London over the present and proposed routes. These are established as follows:

TABLE XXVII

		cents per bushel
Head of Lakes to Montreal		5.27
Montreal to London		6.21
Handling at Montreal		0.75
	Total	12.23

		cents per bushel
Head of Lakes to Buffalo		1.85
Handling at Buffalo		0.75
Buffalo to New York City		3.18
Handling at New York City		0.75
New York City to London		5.81
	Total	12.34

It will be noted there is very little difference in the cost of shipping either via Montreal or through New York City. The rates for the nine-year period from both New York City and Montreal to London were readily available so the London port of destination was used. But there is little difference between the cost of shipping from Montreal or New York City to Liverpool and the cost of shipping from Montreal or New York City to London. The use of London as a point of destination is conservative and places the proposed St. Lawrence seaway at an advantage. The reason is that the cost per bushel-hour, based on the longer number of hours required for shipment from Montreal to London, is less than if it were based upon the number of hours required for the trip from Montreal to Liverpool. This has the effect, in these computations, of making the St. Lawrence route cheaper, because the St. Lawrence rate is constructed on a bushel-hour basis.

By dividing the average cost of 6.21c. a bushel by the 312 hours required to make the trip from Montreal to London, one arrives at 0.02c. per bushel-hour. The total time required for making the trip from Duluth to London over the St. Lawrence would be 457 hours (312 hours on the open ocean and 145 hours along the inland waterway) which, times the cost per bushel-hour, is 9.14c. per bushel. This is the probable minimum rate to be secured for the movement of grain.

By subtracting the constructed rate of 9.14c. per bushel from the present average rate of 12.23, a possible saving of 3.09c. per bushel is indicated.

Export movements of Grain: This is the maximum figure, because it has been assumed, in developing the rate for the movement of grain through the St. Lawrence, that the cost per hour would be the same in the inland waterway as upon the open ocean. Actually there would be additional expenses in the movement of grain-carrying vessels on the inland waterway because of the added insurance costs, extra pilotage, enforced delays resulting from fogs, traffic tie-ups, locks, bridges, etc. Neglecting this, however, we find that the 3.09c. per bushel is equivalent to only $1.03 per ton as against the estimated saving presented in the I. D. report of $2.44 per ton.

The following table lists the movement of United States grain from St. Lawrence and Atlantic ports during the period of 1924 to 1938.

TABLE XXVIII
Export United States Grain. St. Lawrence and Atlantic Ports

YEAR	TOTAL BUSHELS	TOTAL TONS
1924	135,319,000	4,060,000
1925	111,069,000	3,332,000
1926	89,014,000	2,430,000
1927	137,506,000	4,125,000
1928	114,057,000	3,422,000
1929	97,063,000	2,912,000
1930	30,550,000	916,000
1931	28,987,000	870,000
1932	38,964,000	1,169,000
1933	7,496,000	225,000
1934	771,000	23,000
1935	265,000	8,000
1936	3,467,000	104,000
1937	8,502,000	255,000

It will be noted that in 1927 the tonnage was over the four million mark. Since then it has constantly declined and will continue to do so as European, Asiatic, Australian, South American and Canadian areas increase their production. The United States cannot compete in the foreign grain market because of the low labor cost and sub-standard conditions in other major grain-growing countries. In view of the above, it is reasonable to assume that, with the exception of such emergency periods as may temporarily exist because of European conflicts, the grain exportation will not exceed the average of the last eight years. This is equivalent to approximately 446,000 tons.

This tonnage, times the saving of $1.03, is equivalent to a total saving of $459,000 which is nearly six million dollars less than the figure presented in the I. D. report.

For two reasons, this economy of $1.03 a ton (or 3.09c. a bushel) is insufficiently large to accrue to the American farmer or shipper. First, the world's grain prices are set at Liverpool, and a saving of such minuteness would be absorbed by the purchaser in the European market. It would merely enable the buyer to pay less for the grain. Secondly, with the price depressed, foreign grain producers, already operating under standards well below American standards and thereby enjoying an advantage over American producers, could afford to take price cuts in maintaining competition. This would prevent a great increase in the sale of American grain. In brief, the 3.09c. saving is too small to bring the American farmer either an increased price on his product or increased volume in sale.

An example of the price-drop procedure operating in the European market was seen when rail rates from the Middle West to the Atlantic seaboard were reduced on the shipment of winter grain. At that time, the European market dropped its price offer by an equivalent amount because Argentina wheat shippers met the competition. It is the European purchaser, not the American farmer, who would benefit from the 3.09c. differential.

Rubber

It is estimated in the I. D. report that 400,000 tons of rubber are available for shipment into the Akron, Ohio, area. The report indicates a saving of $3.78 per ton in moving this freight by way of the St. Lawrence seaway rather than by rail from New York City. The I. D. report assumes that crude rubber will come from London, England, to New York City at a rate of $1.68 per ton, and thence move by rail to Akron at a cost of $8.00 per ton, or a total of $9.68.

But rubber does not come to the United States from London. Over 90% of it comes from southern and southeastern Asia. It moves 10,172 miles to New York City from Singapore instead of the 3,442 miles from London. This is an important factor because when vessels move over great distances it is necessary to have speed and that requires a narrow beam. Fast ships are more costly to build and operate, so to compete favorably with the slower vessels they have to carry a greater tonnage as well as have greater speed. With their narrow beams, these faster vessels must have room for the needed tonnage in deep drafts. Ships plying from Asiatic ports are of this deep-draft type, because the cost per ton moved in a fast vessel is equal to or less than the cost per ton carried on a slower vessel. This gives the fast boat a very decided advantage on long trips.

Motor ships and steamers bringing rubber from the Straits Settlements to New York City are from ten to twelve-thousand-ton vessels operating on a twenty-five to twenty-six foot draft. This fact alone is sufficient to strike out entirely the estimate for importation of rubber via the St. Lawrence seaway because the canal would not physically accommodate vessels of that draft. Furthermore, these deep-draft vessels do not carry shipments entirely of rubber. They carry miscellaneous freight and must obtain full loads both ways to operate at a profit. The more greatly diversified market of New York City offers a much better assurance of full cargo capacities inbound and outbound than do the Great Lakes ports.

Because vessels carrying crude rubber to Atlantic ports could not navigate the proposed St. Lawrence seaway, because full cargoes both ways are so essential on such long hauls and because it would be impractical to duplicate New York's exchange and marketing facilities in the Great Lakes area for only 42% of the year, it is logical to assume that importation of rubber by way of the St. Lawrence seaway should not be considered.

In the interest of complete fairness, however, and to cover any possible importation of some small quantities, an allowance of 100,000 tons has been made, resulting in a total saving of $485,000, predicated upon a saving of $4.85 per ton. This saving was determined by using the existing rate of $18 per ton from the Straits Settlements to New York City, which is equivalent to $0.0177 per ton hour. This factor, multiplied by the 1059 hours required for the trip to Cleveland from the Straits Settlements, amounts to $18.75. To this figure was added a rail rate of $3.00 from Cleveland to Akron, making a total cost of $21.75 as compared with the present cost of $26.60 if shipped by way of New York City.

Flour and Meal

The I. D. report estimates that 859,000 tons of flour and meal are available for movement from Minneapolis to Liverpool through the St. Lawrence seaway based on a twelve-month period. The yardstick route used for comparison with the St. Lawrence is the one from Minneapolis to New York by rail, and thence to Liverpool. The I. D. report states that the present cost of shipping through New York is $9.21 per ton, that the cost of shipping by way of the St. Lawrence seaway would be $4.73 and that the saving would be $4.48 per ton.

The first thing to consider in analyzing this particular commodity is whether or not Minneapolis is, by virtue of its position, the logical location of a flour milling center for export purposes. If it is not, the estimated tonnage available for movement through the St. Lawrence seaway is vitally affected.

This report, therefore, analyzes the cost of delivering to Liverpool flour milled at both Minneapolis and Buffalo. The shipping rate on wheat from Duluth to Buffalo is 1.85c. per bushel or $0.62 per ton. The rail rate from Buffalo to New York City is $3.20 per ton, and the rate from New York City to Liverpool is approximately $3.40 per ton. Milling at Buffalo would require one additional handling over milling at Minneapolis. This is equivalent to approximately 25c. per ton. The summation of these items shows that the cost of shipping flour milled at Buffalo, delivered by rail to New York City and thence to Liverpool, would amount to $7.47.

There is another way, however, of routing flour to Liverpool from Buffalo. This is via the existing Erie Canal which carries considerable flour tonnage as indicated on the following page:

TABLE XXIX

	Flour
1932	30,200 tons
1933	106,456 ”
1934	78,842 ”
1935	53,981 ”
1937	38,292 ”
1938	43,686 ”

The following breakdown shows that cost of moving wheat to Buffalo, and of moving flour, after milling at Buffalo, to New York City via the Erie Canal, and thence to Liverpool:

TABLE XXX

	per ton
Wheat, Duluth to Buffalo	$0.62
Flour, Buffalo to New York via Canal	1.06
Flour, New York to Liverpool	3.40
Extra Handling	0.25
Total	$5.33

The analysis below shows the estimated cost of moving flour from Minneapolis to Chicago, and thence to Liverpool via the proposed St. Lawrence seaway.

TABLE XXXI

		per ton
Minneapolis to Chicago (I. D. report p. 125)		$2.30
Chicago to Liverpool	(See below)	4.39
Total		$6.69

Cost per ton-hour for shipping flour =

$$\frac{\$3.40 \text{ (cost per ton New York to Liverpool)}}{322 \text{ hours (New York to Liverpool)}} = \$0.0106 \text{ per ton-hour}$$

Hours — Chicago to Liverpool =

135 hrs. Chicago to Montreal

279 hrs. Montreal to Liverpool

Total   414 hrs.

414 x $0.0106 per ton-hour = $4.39

The above analysis shows that shipments of Minneapolis flour to Liverpool, over the proposed St. Lawrence seaway route, would cost $6.69 per ton, compared with $5.33 per ton for shipment of Buffalo flour, via the Erie Canal route. In other words, Buffalo flour could be delivered at Liverpool for $1.36 less than Minneapolis flour.

The above would indicate that movement of flour from Minneapolis to Liverpool by way of the St. Lawrence seaway should not be an important element in considering the economic feasibility of the St. Lawrence Seaway Project. It is assumed, however, that some flour will move over the St. Lawrence seaway from Minneapolis and the following analysis has been prepared to show the possible saving in shipping flour that way.

TABLE XXXII
Estimated Cost Minneapolis to Liverpool Via Present Route

	per ton
Minneapolis to Chicago (present rail)	$2.60
Chicago to New York via Motorship (including handling)	5.20
New York City to Liverpool	3.40
Total	$11.20

Estimated Cost Minneapolis to Liverpool via Proposed Seaway

	per ton
Minneapolis to Chicago (present rail)	$2.60
Chicago to Liverpool (see previous)	4.39
Total	$6.99

Thus the present rate of $11.20 is $4.21 per ton more costly than over the proposed St. Lawrence seaway route. The I. D. report states that the saving would be $4.48. According to this, the actual saving would be 6% less than stated in the I. D. report.

Export Movements of Flour: In order to get the total possible saving in the shipment of flour, the next step was to estimate the probable tonnage. The I. D. report uses 859,000 tons, which, as the following analysis will show, is too high.

The total United States exports of flour for the years 1929 to 1938 inclusive were:

TABLE XXXIII
United States Flour Exports

1929	1,338,974
1930	1,279,880
1931	946,092
1932	567,910
1933	388,472
1934	407,974
1935	416,304
1936	358,680
1937	436,296
1938	510,874

The average annual exportation of flour for those years amounted to 665,146 tons. Investigation has shown that other meals represent approximately 20% of the flour exportation; therefore, there was an average annual export of approximately 831,000 tons of flour and meal for the years 1929 to 1938 inclusive.

Further investigation demonstrates that approximately 40% of the total United States flour and meal are shipped from the North Atlantic ports. Therefore, from the years 1929 to 1938, an average of approximately 325,000 tons of flour and meal were exported from these ports. The export business from Minneapolis which might eventually use the St. Lawrence seaway route is now using the northern Atlantic ports. Since this is the case, the I. D. estimate of 859,000 tons of flour and meal available for shipment from Minneapolis to Liverpool is far out of line.

Since flour produced in Buffalo has the advantage over flour produced in Minneapolis for export, most of the available 325,000 tons for export from the north Atlantic ports is shipped from Buffalo and other eastern milling centers. Consequently, it is believed that an estimate of 25% of this tonnage assigned to Minneapolis would be a liberal allowance. This amounts to 81,000 tons, which, times the estimated saving of $4.21 per ton, is equivalent to $341,000.

Iron and Steel

It is estimated, in the I. D. report, that 635,000 tons of iron and steel are available for movement from Chicago to Rio de Janeiro at an estimated saving of $5.84 per ton. The report states that the present rate of shipping is $9.47 and that the rate via the proposed seaway would be $3.63.

The following analysis indicates that again these figures are optimistic. In the first place, only small quantities of iron and steel products are shipped from New York City to South America. Exports to the entire east coast of South America for the period 1929 to 1935 are shown in the following table:

TABLE XXXIV

Shipments to South American East Coast Ports		*Exports to Brazil*	
Year	*Tons*	*Year*	*Tons*
1929	148,291	1929	60,704
1932	21,460	1932	5,681
1933	92,580	1933	47,972
1934	120,367	1934	41,456
1935	63,102	1935	37,575

The cost of shipping by the present route from Chicago to New York City, via Erie Canal, and thence to Rio de Janeiro is as follows:

TABLE XXXV

	per ton
Chicago to Buffalo (including loading on Barge Canal)	$1.50
Buffalo to New York City, via Barge (including handling at New York)	1.75
New York City to Rio de Janeiro	4.00
Total	$7.25

The cost per ton-hour on the ocean route would amount to $0.00839. Since it requires 671 hours for the journey from Rio de Janeiro to Chicago, the rate by way of the seaway would be $5.63. Thus the saving of shipping to Rio de Janeiro would be $1.62 per ton.

It does not appear that the estimated 635,000 tons shown in the I. D. report would come from the Chicago area. It is far more likely that most of the export iron and steel would come from mills in the east. The steel mills at Sparrows Point, Maryland, can ship to Rio de Janeiro for $4.00 per ton as against the projected rate of $5.63 from Chicago. For the sake of conservatism, the I. D. tonnage figure was used in this report. This amount, times the estimated saving of $1.62 per ton, is equal to $1,029,000, or 72% of that claimed in the I. D. report.

Agricultural Implements

Farm implements to the extent of 198,000 tons are claimed, in the I. D. report, as being available for movement from Chicago to Liverpool at a saving of $8.85 per ton. That report states the present cost of shipping is $11.89, and that the proposed rate would be $3.04 per ton.

Agricultural implements are now shipped from Chicago to New York City, via motorship over Erie Canal, for $3.75 per ton including handling at New York City, and the rate from New York to Liverpool is $5.00. Thus the present cost is $8.75. Based on the rate from New York City to Liverpool, the cost of shipping this product from Chicago by way of the St. Lawrence would be $6.42 per ton, as the shipping rate is $0.0155 per ton-hour and it requires 414 hours from Chicago to Liverpool. Thus the saving would be $2.33 instead of the $8.85 figure shown in the I. D. report.

The following table shows the agricultural implement export tonnages for all the north Atlantic ports, from 1929 to 1938:

TABLE XXXVI

Year		Tons
1929	....	48,778
1932	....	19,393
1933	....	10,626
1934	....	11,993
1935	....	14,811
1938	....	66,874
	Total	172,475

The average for the six years shown is 29,000 tons and is indicative that the I. D. report estimate of 198,000 tons is greatly exaggerated. It has been assumed in this report that Chicago would receive the benefit of all farm implement exports shown by the North Atlantic ports average. This is equivalent to a total saving of $68,000 instead of the $1,752,300 given in the I. D. report.

Automobiles

The I. D. report lists 566,000 tons of automobiles and parts available for movement from the Detroit area to Liverpool over the proposed seaway. It indicates that the present cost of shipping is $17.58 as against a proposed $5.41, with a net saving of $12.17.

Automobiles are moved by rail from Detroit to New York City for $9.60 per ton and from there to Liverpool (including handling at New York City) for $4.40, making a total of $14.00.

The ocean rate per ton-hour is equivalent to $0.0137, which figure was obtained by dividing the number of hours between New York City and Liverpool into $4.40. This rate per ton-hour, multiplied by 356 (hours required to Detroit), is equivalent to $4.88. This, compared with the aforementioned $14.00 present rate, would indicate a saving of $9.12.

This, however, is not as important a saving as it may seem, because the present rate includes $9.60 for rail movement from Detroit to New York City. At present the Government is raising all bridges six feet on the Oswego Canal and the easterly end of the New York State Barge Canal. This work will be completed in two years. It will then be possible to move automobiles from Detroit to New York City on motorships along with other cargoes. Conferences with motorship operators have brought out the fact that they will be in a position to move automobiles from Detroit to New York City for $5.00 per ton after the bridges have been raised. The cost of shipping cars from Detroit to Liverpool then will be $9.40; that is $5.00 per ton Detroit to New York City and $4.40 New York City to Liverpool. This is $4.52 more than the constructed St. Lawrence rate of $4.88.

It seems unlikely that auto tonnage would use the seaway to any great extent, even though there were a substantial saving, because cars are shipped in small lots to many different ports. The shipping of cars is unlike that of grain where one vessel will carry a full load to Liverpool or London. In the case of automobiles, a few go to many different ports in Europe, Asia, Africa, South America, etc. Consequently, the point of shipment for cars must be a port of entry for ships from all over the globe. The Great Lakes area would not have vessels from as many different foreign ports as does New York City, nor would the Great Lakes ports have New York City's frequency of call. Consequently, cars would continue to move primarily by way of New York City and other large Atlantic ports.

In addition, practically all automobile manufacturing companies have assembly plants near these eastern ports and it would be natural to export cars from these assembly points rather than from the interior of the country.

An allowance was made, though, for the shipment of some cars from Detroit via the St. Lawrence seaway. This was taken as being equal to the tonnage shipped in 1937 to the United Kingdom, Belgium, Sweden, Norway, Holland and the Irish Free State. The reason for the selection of these countries is that the distance by way of the St. Lawrence seaway to areas south of the Mediterranean area is greater than from the Port of New York.

In 1937, 113,000 tons of cars moved to the countries of northern Europe. This tonnage, times the estimated savings of $9.12, represents a total saving of $1,031,000.

Packing House Products

The I. D. report estimates that 140,000 tons of packing house products would move from Chicago to Liverpool through the proposed St. Lawrence seaway. It further estimates there would be a saving of $8.35 per ton, amounting to a total saving of $1,169,000.

Investigations similar to those revealed in the preceding paragraphs show that both the savings and the probable tonnage are too optimistic.

At present, packing house products are moving by motorship from Chicago to Oswego and over the Erie Canal to New York City for $3.50 per ton. There is a handling charge of approximately 50c. per ton in New York City. The rate from New York City to Liverpool is $7.00 per ton. Thus the combined present rate of shipping from Chicago to Liverpool is $11.00 per ton.

Inasmuch as approximately 322 hours are required between New York City and Liverpool, the cost per ton-hour is equivalent to $0.0221. This times the estimated time of 414 hours for shipping from Chicago to Liverpool is equivalent to a charge of $9.15 per ton.

The difference between this figure and the present rate of $11.00 is $1.85, the maximum saving by shipping these products through the proposed St.

Lawrence seaway.   This amount is approximately 78% less than the indicated saving in the I. D. report.

The following table shows exportation of meat products from all North Atlantic ports, from 1932 to 1935 and for the year 1938:

TABLE XXXVII

Year	Tons
1932	59,238
1933	72,844
1934	83,459
1935	51,877
1938	47,122

These figures show that the I. D. report estimate of 140,000 tons is far above the actual shipments from north Atlantic ports in past years.   The average of export figures from North Atlantic ports is 63,000 tons.   Assuming that Chicago would receive all of these exports, we find the total savings would only amount to $117,000 as compared with the estimated savings of over one million dollars shown in the I. D. report.

Summary of Apparent Savings
TABLE XXXVIII

Tonnage and Estimated Savings of Commodities Studied—Twelve Months Basis

Imports	Interdepartmental Report			Niagara Frontier Planning Board		
	Tonnage	Savings Per Ton	Total Savings	Tonnage	Savings Per Ton	Total Savings
Bananas	740,000	$11.67	$8,635,800		$0.00	
Sugar to Chicago	630,000	5.08	3,200,400	410,000	0.76	312,000
Sugar to Minneapolis	625,000	6.05	3,781,250	406,000	0.80	325,000
Coffee	280,000	5.76	1,612,800	224,000	3.17	710,000
Kaolin	140,000	1.01	141,400	45,000	1.72	77,000
Rubber	400,000	3.78	1,512,000	100,000	4.85	485,000
Total	2,815,000		$18,883,650	1,185,000		$1,909,000
Average		$ 5.56			$1.88	
Exports						
Grain (Wheat Basis) Duluth	2,618,000	$ 2.44	$ 6,387,920	446,000	$1.03	$ 459,000
Flour—Meal	859,000	4.48	3,848,320	81,000	4.21	341,000
Iron and Steel	635,000	5.84	3,708,400	635,000	1.62	1,029,000
Agricultural Implements	198,000	8.85	1,752,300	29,000	2.33	68,000
Autos and Parts	566,000	12.17	6,888,220	113,000	9.12	1,031,000
Packing House	140,000	8.35	1,169,000	63,000	1.85	117,000
Totals	5,016,000		$23,754,160	1,367,000		$3,045,000
Average		$ 7.02			$3.36	
Grand Total	7,831,000		$42,637,810	2,552,000		$4,954,000

The total savings of the commodities studied is $37,683,810 less than claimed in the I. D. report.

The preceding table is a recapitulation of the I. D. report's estimate of tonnage, savings per ton, and total savings together with this report's estimate of tonnage, saving per ton and total savings. These are the studied commodities, or, in other words, the commodities which the Government studied in formulating the I. D. report. The Niagara Frontier Planning Board checked against them and these are the summarized results.

It will be noted in the above table that only 2,552,000 tons (twelve-months basis) is likely to be moved over the proposed St. Lawrence seaway at an estimated saving of $4,954,000. Let it be understood, however, that this includes only the studied commodities.

The I. D. report averages the probable savings on imports and exports of these studied commodities and then generally applies those average savings to "All Other Important Commodities." It has been shown in this Niagara Frontier Planning Board survey that I. D. tonnages, as well as savings, must be greatly reduced. In the following table, therefore, the tonnages for those commodities which were not studied (i. e. "All Other Important Commodities") are reduced by the same percentage as was applied to those which were studied. The new probable tonnages were multiplied by the average savings of the studied commodities to obtain the total savings.

TABLE XXXIX

Recapitulation of Tonnages and Possible Savings

	Probable Tonnage in			Average Indicated Savings	Total Indicated Savings
	I. D Tonnage	% of I. D. Tonnage	Probable Tonnage		
Imports Studied...............	2,815,000	42.0	1,185,000		$ 1,909,000
All other Import Commodities	5,798,500	42.0	2,435,000	$1.88	4,578,000
Subtotal Imports	8,613,500		3,620,000		6,487,000
Exports Studied...............	5,016,000	27.3	1,367,000		3,045,000
All other Export Commodities .	6,191,200	27.3	1,690,000	$3.36	5,679,000
Subtotal Exports	11,207,200		3,057,000		$ 8,724,000
Grand Total	19,820,700		6,677,000		$15,211,000
After deducting 42% for Closed Season.....................	11,496,000		3,873,000		$ 8,822,000

It will be noted above that the grand total of probable tonnages available to the St. Lawrence seaway, based on the twelve month's period, is equal to 6,677,000 tons. If the St. Lawrence seaway were open twelve months of the year this would be equivalent to a saving of $15,211,000 over present transportation systems. But the St. Lawrence is closed for 42% of the year, so both tonnages and the apparent savings must be reduced by that percentage. Consequently, the maximum possible saving of the St. Lawrence seaway would be $8,822,000.

Summary of Estimated Savings

The opening up of the Great Lakes to foreign carriers would mean that American lake and canal transportation systems and American railroads would have to meet the competition of low standard foreign labor.

It is not the contention of the Niagara Frontier Planning Board that the proposed St. Lawrence seaway would not offer a cheaper mode of transportation for certain bulk commodities. The question is whether these savings are sufficiently large to justify the original expense of the project and the shift of business from established routes to the suggested new route, and therefore the first step is to determine what these savings will be.

In 1934, the government published an Interdepartmental Report which revealed the findings of a survey into the economic effects of the proposed St. Lawrence navigation development. The Niagara Frontier Planning Board made an exhaustive study of these Interdepartmental Report conclusions. The Board found that the government's figures were in most instances way out of line with existing conditions. The analysis demonstrated that the Interdepartmental Report had proceeded to set up yardsticks which were based on a group of selected commodities and then applied to all other commodities in reaching a sum for savings in transportation costs of shipments via the St. Lawrence route.

But the Interdepartmental Report arrived at an exaggerated savings figure because it failed, in many instances, to use the cheapest present route in comparing shipping costs between current transportation media and the proposed St. Lawrence route. Furthermore, the report did not employ accurate standards in constructing what the probable St. Lawrence seaway commercial rates would be. As a result, the differential between shipping costs over the St. Lawrence as against shipping costs over current lines is excessively estimated in the Interdepartmental survey.

When a study of these government findings shows the suggested transportation rate economies to be inaccurate, the estimates of volume of traffic over the projected seaway must likewise be revised. The figure for tonnage of cargoes which might move through the St. Lawrence is largely dependent upon the savings. This is true because of the principle that lower transportation costs would increase the market where the goods could be sold. Expressed another way, this principle simply means that when commodities can be more cheaply shipped, they can be carried farther without increasing the price to the consumer. Thus it is seen that the market is broadened, so more goods can be sold. The greater the saving, the greater the volume.

The Niagara Frontier Planning Board, consequently, not only adjusted the item for savings, but also logically followed this by changing the item for tonnages in accordance with the new total for savings.

The Interdepartmental Report also shows aberrations in its use of current United States import and export figures for various commodities. Enquiry into other government statistics on this subject disclosed the Interdepartmental Report's failing. Certain revisions were necessary in this phase of the matter also.

In every instance of revision, though, the Niagara Frontier Planning Board strived to avoid changes which were not entirely within minimum demands.

The Interdepartmental Report set the probable seaway traffic volume at 11,496,000 tons annually and the savings at $78,893,130 annually. Actually, it was found that these aggregates should be 3,873,000 for estimated seaway tonnage and $8,822,000 for estimated savings in seaway transportation costs.

PROBABLE LOSSES

Damage to Current Transportation Interests — Loss to American Owners of Ocean-going Vessels — Necessary Deductions — Indirect Losses — Loss to Coal Industry — Diversion of Canadian Grain — Annual Costs of Maintenance, Operation, Interest and Amortization — Comparison of Savings with Losses — Loss to United States Transportation Based on Tonnage and Routes Used in I. D. Report — Railroads — Inland Waterways — Combined Losses — Loss to American Ocean Shipping Based on I. D. Tonnage — Possible Savings Based on I. D. Tonnage and Routes — Present Rates — Possible Per Ton Savings — Savings Based on Studied Commodities — Effect on Coastwise Shipping — Summary.

Damage to Current Transportation Interests

THE possible savings in shipping costs, however, do not represent net savings because there would be an accompanying loss to existing American transportation systems now carrying this tonnage in the United States and from Atlantic Seaboard ports. In the various preceding paragraphs where particular commodities were studied in detail, rates were given for the movement of those commodities over the present and cheapest transportation routes. These rates and handling charges, multiplied by the estimated tonnages which might be shipped through the St. Lawrence seaway, will show the loss in gross earnings to currently established transportation systems in this country.

The following table lists the imports and exports studied, the loss per ton to United States transportation systems, the tonnage estimates as possibly available for St. Lawrence seaway movement and the total loss per item.

TABLE XL

Yearly Loss to Transportation on the Various Studied Commodities Based on Niagara Frontier Planning Board's Estimated Tonnages and Present Rates via Cheapest Routes

Imports	Per Ton Loss to Transportation	Probable Tonnage	Loss
Bananas		none	
Sugar, Chicago......................	$5.00	410,000	$ 2,050,000
Sugar, Minneapolis................	5.20	406,000	2,111,000
Coffee	5.40	224,000	1,210,000
Kaolin..............................	2.00	45,000	90,000
Rubber	5.60	100,000	560,000
Total Imports		1,185,000	$ 6,021,000
Average......................	$4.64		
Exports			
Grain, Duluth	$2.18	446,000	$ 972,000
Flour and Meal	5.20	81,000	421,000
Iron and Steel	3.25	635,000	2,064,000
Agricultural Implements	3.75	29,000	109,000
Autos and Parts...........	9.60	113,000	1,085,000
Packing House Products	4.00	63,000	252,000
Total Exports......................		1,367,000	$ 4,903,000
Average...........................	$4.66		
GRAND TOTAL		2,552,000	$10,924,000

The above table shows that on a twelve-month basis, the total loss on studied imports amounts to $6,021,000 and the total loss on studied exports,

$4,903,000, or a total of $10,924,000. Note that this includes only certain commodities as listed.

By applying the average loss of $4.64 per ton for imports and the average loss of $4.66 per ton for exports (as shown in the preceding table) to all other tonnage, estimates of the probable losses resulting from the movement of these commodities over the St. Lawrence seaway can be obtained. The following table shows these other losses together with those listed above.

TABLE XLI

Yearly Loss to Transportation on Studied and Unstudied Commodities Based on Niagara Frontier Planning Board's Estimated Tonnages and Present Rates via Cheapest Route

Imports	Average Per Ton Loss	Tonnage	Total Loss
Studied		1,185,000	$ 6,021,000
All Others........................	$4.64	2,435,000	11,298,000
Total Imports		3,620,000	$17,319,000
Exports			
Studied		1,367,000	$ 4,903,000
All Others........................	$4.66	1,690,000	7,875,000
Total Exports....................		3,057,000	$12,778,000
GRAND TOTAL		6,677,000	$30,097,000
After deducting 42% for Closed Season ...		3,873,000	$17,456,000

The above table demonstrates that the loss to United States transportation systems would amount to $17,319,000 on imports and $12,778,000 on exports, or a total of $30,097,000. These amounts are founded on a twelve-month movement of 6,677,000 tons. Corrected for the closed season on the St. Lawrence (42%), the loss to United States transportation systems would be 3,873,000 tons which is equivalent to $17,456,000 in revenue.

Loss to American Owners of Ocean-Going Vessels

Transportation systems currently established in the United States would not alone suffer from a diversion of traffic through a St. Lawrence seaway. There would also be losses for owners of American ocean-going vessels who now handle trade at American seaports but whose ships could not navigate the proposed seaway. The damage to them is determined by applying the existing ocean rate to the probable tonnage loss.

The following tables set up annual losses on studied and unstudied commodities in accordance with the plan of figuring used above for inland transportation.

It will be noted from the following tables that the average loss on the studied imports is equivalent to $5.64 per ton and on the exports $4.29 per ton. The total import losses, on all commodities, amounts to $19,063,000; on exports the loss is $12,013,000, or a combined loss of $31,076,000.

TABLE XLII

Yearly Loss to American Ocean Vessel Owners on Studied Commodities Based on Niagara Frontier Planning Board's Estimated Tonnage

Imports	Per Ton Loss	Probable Tonnages	Loss
Bananas			
Sugar, Chicago	$ 2.00	410,000	$ 820,000
Sugar, Minneapolis	2.00	406,000	812,000
Coffee	7 63	224,000	1,709,000
Kaolin	4.20	45,000	189,000
Rubber	18.00	100,000	1,800,000
Total		1,185,000	$ 5,330,000
Average	$5.64		
Exports			
Grain	$ 1.94	446,000	$ 865,000
Flour and Meal	3.40	81,000	275,000
Iron and Steel	4.00	635,000	2,540,000
Agricultural Implements	5.00	29,000	145,000
Autos and Parts	4.40	113,000	497,000
Packing House Products	7.00	63,000	441,000
Total		1,367,000	$ 4,763,000
Average	$ 4.29		
Grand Total		2,552,000	$10,093,000

TABLE XLIII

Yearly Loss to American Ocean Vessel Owners on Studied and Unstudied Commodities Based on Niagara Frontier Planning Board's Estimated Tonnages

Imports	Average Per Ton Loss	Tonnage	Loss
Studied		1,185,000	$ 5,330,000
All Others	$ 5.64	2,435,000	13,733,000
Total		3,620,000	$19,063,000
Exports			
Studied		1,367,000	$ 4,763,000
All Others	$ 4.29	1,690,000	7,250,000
Total		3,057,000	$12,013,000
Grand Total		6,677,000	$31,076,000

Deduction for Closed Season (42%) $18,024,000.
Loss to American Vessels (deduct 65%) $6,308,000.
Deduction for American Vessels which could use St. Lawrence (45%) $3,470,000.

Necessary Deductions: Certain deductions must be made from this combined loss of $31,076,000 because it is predicated on a twelve-month basis. Furthermore, this figure assumes that all the seaway tonnage diverted from

Atlantic ports would have been carried in American-owned sea-going ships if the seaway didn't exist, while as a matter of fact some of it would have been sent from Atlantic ports on foreign vessels anyway. The $31,076,000 sum also assumes that absolutely none of these American-owned ocean ships could use the deepened waterway. In adjusting this total, then, a deduction of 42%, as has been derived previously in this Niagara Frontier Planning Board Report, must be made for the closed season. This drops the amount to $18,024,000. Investigations of the 1937 Report of the Department of Commerce (entitled "Foreign Commerce and Navigation of the United States", p. 757) indicates that only about 35% of the tonnage exported and imported at North Atlantic ports was carried in American-owned vessels. A further deduction of 65% must be made to account for this. The total figure thereby becomes $6,308,000.

A further deduction is necessary to allow for United States ocean vessels, trading at North Atlantic ports, which could use the St. Lawrence seaway. It has been shown previously in this report that 62% of the tonnage of all American-owned vessels operating out of North Atlantic ports could not use the St. Lawrence. This would lead to the conclusion that a deduction of 38% would have to be made, because this percentage represents ships which could use the seaway and cargoes therefore might not be diverted from them.

However, these percentages cannot be accepted on their face value because they refer only to ships having speeds of twelve knots or over. Most of the American ocean-going ships are in this category, but in order to allow for vessels under this speed capacity which might use the St. Lawrence, the 38% figure is adjusted to 45% and a deduction is made accordingly.

This percentage puts the net loss to American ocean vessels at $3,470,000. Added to the loss of the United States inland transportation systems, it makes a total damage of $20,926,000 as against a possible saving of $8,822,000. The net direct loss to present American transportation systems, therefore, is $12,104,000. To this net direct loss must be added others which are subsequently described.

Indirect Losses

Loss to Coal Industry: The Dominion of Canada is the largest customer for American coal. Approximately 17,000,000 tons annually (some 14,000,000 tons of bituminous coal and 3,000,000 tons of anthracite) are shipped to Canada from Pennsylvania, Ohio, Virginia, West Virginia, and Kentucky. Of this, approximately 7,000,000 tons are shipped in Great Lakes vessels to Canadian ports.

If the St. Lawrence seaway were constructed, shippers from Europe would send great quantities of coal into the Great Lakes area and thereby cut into the Canadian coal market now served by American producers. This would be a natural procedure because the vessel-owners must carry cargoes in the west-ward movement across the Atlantic to exchange for United States and Canadian exports. The figures show that Canada and the United States would export some 6,446,000 tons of grain (on a 12-months basis) each year down the St. Lawrence. Virtually all of this would go to Europe. Consequently, grain vessel-owners would find that they must ship an equivalent amount of commodities over to the Great Lakes from abroad.

Europe's natural resources would make coal the logical product to be sent over here as ballast cargo. Furthermore, coal can easily be carried in grain ships. Thus it is inevitable that coal would account for almost all of the cargoes shipped into the Great Lakes in exchange for grain. Canada would be the natural market for most of this coal, so the effect would be the dumping of European coal in Canada as a means of meeting United States as well as Canadian exports. Adjusted to the open navigation season by the reduction of 42%, European imports in exchange for grain must approximate 3,700,000 tons. This would result in an annual loss of some $13,000,000 to the United States coal mines and coal transportation interests.

Diversion of Canadian Grain: Great quantities of Canadian export grain now move through the United States. If the St. Lawrence seaway became a reality, this grain would largely move through that waterway. The following table shows the export of Canadian grain through the United States north Atlantic ports from 1924 to 1931 inclusive. For the period of 1932 to 1937, the amounts are not shown because during that time there was a six-cent preferential on Canadian grain shipped to the United Kingdom through Canadian ports. As a result, Canadian grain did not move through the United States to any great extent. In 1938, the preferential was removed and Canadian grain once again was transported through the United States in large quantities. However, the amounts were not readily available and therefore were not included in the table.

TABLE XLIV
Canadian Grain Exported through North Atlantic United States Ports.

BUSHELS

Year	Portland	Boston	New York	Phila.	Baltimore	Hampton Roads	Total
1924	8,344,000	3,511,000	67,575,000	20,824,000	13,213,000	2,986,000	116,453,000
1925	7,065,000	6,166,000	91,657,000	23,528,000	12,273,000	330,000	141,019,000
1926	8,244,000	4,919,000	79,159,000	16,966,000	13,551,000	670,000	123,509,000
1927	4,979,000	2,235,000	81,447,000	13,046,000	12,278,000	779,000	114,764,000
1928	2,005,000	4,413,000	66,292,000	8,037,000	14,910,000	210,000	95,867,000
1929	2,815,000	5,337,000	71,388,000	11,669,000	20,631,000	1,020,000	112,860,000
1930	961,000	777,000	49,663,000	2,719,000	4,083,000		58,203,000
1931	1,170,000	3,567,000	60,249,000	4,809,000	6,997,000	337,000	77,129,000
						Total	839,804,000

Average for eight years—104,976,000 bushels = 3,150,000 tons

The rate from the head of the Great Lakes to New York City, including elevating, is 6.53c. per bushel, or $2.18 per ton. Thus, the total loss on a twelve-month basis would be $6,867,000 and corrected for the closed season of navigation $3,983,000. In event Canadian grain moved through the proposed seaway, there would be an additional loss to United States ocean shipping interests equivalent to $6,111,000, based on the rate of 5.81c. per bushel, or $1.94 per ton, from New York to London. This amount, when reduced by 42% (for closed navigation season), 65% and then by 45% (see page 77) to determine the net loss, is $682,000. Added to the $3,983,000, it makes a total of $4,665,000 in revenue which now goes to United States interests from Canadian grain movements but which would not be realized in the future.

Of course, not all Canadian grain movements follow the all-water route to New York City for export. They go to Portland, Boston, Philadelphia and other north Atlantic ports by rail as well as by water to New York City. However, these alternate routes are more costly ones to follow, therefore, the selection of the Buffalo-New York route in determining losses to established transportation routes gives a minimum figure.

Annual Costs of Maintenance, Operation, Interest and Amortization

In the section entitled "Total Cost of Development United States and Canada, Including Interest During The Amortization Period, Maintenance and Operation," it was shown that the total United States cost would be $623,221,000. By dividing this amount by fifty years, we reach the annual cost of $12,464,000.

The table below sets up the annual losses described in the preceding paragraphs based upon the Niagara Frontier Planning Board's estimate of tonnage moved over the St. Lawrence seaway.

TABLE XLV

Summary of Losses Based on Niagara Frontier Planning Board's Estimate of Use of the St. Lawrence Seaway

Annual Costs
Interest, Amortization, Operation and Maintenance, $\dfrac{\$623,221,000}{50} =$ $12,464,000

Loss to United States Inland Transportation System	17,456,000
Loss to United States Ocean Carriers.	3,470,000
Loss from Diverting Canadian Grain from United States Routes and Ocean Ships	4,665,000
Loss to United States Coal Industry resulting from Foreign Competition.	13,000,000
Total.	$51,055,000
Less Possible Savings.	8,822,000
Annual Net Loss.	$42,233,000

It will be noted that the total annual loss to the United States transportation and affiliated industries amounts to $51,055,000 against a possible saving of $8,822,000 resulting in a net yearly loss of over forty-two million dollars.

Comparison of Savings with Losses: The net loss of more than $42,000,000, of course, is a loss to interests in the United States. Further explanation of this finding is necessary, however, to show the justification for the comparison of these losses with the savings which would accrue because of the difference in transportation rates between the St. Lawrence route and present routes.

If the new water-borne commerce, which it is assumed will be created in the St. Lawrence River, were to go to American vessel-owners, it would not be a proper procedure to ignore that new commerce in arriving at a net loss figure. In other words, the diversion of business from present transportation lines to the St. Lawrence would simply result in a transfer of earning power from one American medium to another American medium. But the fact is that the vessel owners who presumably would gain from trade through the St. Lawrence (i.e., vessel owners who would obtain additional revenue which now goes to railroads and inland water carriers in this country) are not domestic operators. They are foreigners.

It has already been shown that ships of United States registry which could use the proposed Seaway comprise only 5% of the world's merchant vessel tonnage. In arriving at a figure for the net loss to United States enterprises, it would appear to be proper to make a deduction as an allowance for this new business which would be enjoyed by American ship owners. The final result, though, would find this deduction absorbed in another way. This is so because it cannot be assumed that all of the savings in transportation costs (i.e., the differential between rates over the proposed seaway and rates over currently existing lines of commerce) would accrue to the buyer and seller in the United States. Much of the differential would go to foreign consumers and sellers.

It has already been pointed out in this report that virtually all of the differential in grain shipments would redound to the purchaser in Europe. A similar result is found in regard to other products, although not to so great an extreme. Despite this fact, the Niagara Frontier Planning Board has included these full amounts in its estimates of savings to American interests, so whatever new business would be found on the St. Lawrence by American vessel operators is accounted for through these excessive savings figures.

The question may be raised: "Why wouldn't American shipowners build more smaller draft carriers so that they could get a larger share of this new St. Lawrence business?" The answer is that the standards of American ship construction and ship operation are so high that the American vessel-owner couldn't profitably build and run craft of the type necessary to compete with the foreign tramps. Only 30% of the vessels handling the import and export business of the United States today are American owned. Most of these are too large to use the proposed seaway, but the 30% figure is impressive because it demonstrates how generally unprofitable it is for American craft to compete with foreign craft. The situation is especially acute with regard to small tramp steamers, the sort of vessels which would ply the St. Lawrence.

Loss to United States Transportation Systems on Tonnages and Routes Used in I. D. Report

Because the I. D. report's estimates on the volume of traffic likely to use the proposed St. Lawrence seaway are considerably higher than those of the Niagara Frontier Planning Board, the losses which present transportation systems in this country would suffer because of diversion of shipping from their lines through the St. Lawrence are proportionately higher when based on I. D. figures. The greater the diversion of traffic through the St. Lawrence, the greater the damage to existing commercial routes.

Herewith presented is data showing what the losses would be if the I. D. estimates became realized. As previously stated, these I. D. tonnage figures are too high, but it is deemed advisable, in the interest of completeness, to demonstrate what those figures would mean to established transportation interests in the United States.

TABLE XLVI
Loss to Rails on Studied and Unstudied Commodities Based on Tonnages and Routes Used in I. D. Report and Present Rates

STUDIED

IMPORTS	RATE PER TON	TONNAGE LOST	LOSS
Bananas	$17.40	740,000	$12,876,000
Sugar, Chicago (water loss)	—	—	—
Sugar, Minneapolis (water loss)	—	—	—
Coffee (water loss)	—	—	—
Kaolin ($6.80–$4.80)	2.00	140,000	280,000
Rubber ($8.60–$3.00)	5.60	400,000	2,240.000
Total Imports		1,280,000	$15,396,000
Average	$8.33		
% of total imports studied, moved by rail	$\frac{1,280,000}{2,815,000} \times 100 =$		45.5%

EXPORTS			
Grain—Duluth (water loss)	—	—	—
Flour and Meal ($7.60–$2.60)	$5.00	859,000	$4,295,000
Iron and Steel	7.48	635,000	4,750,000
Agricultural Implements	9.00	198,000	1,782,000
Autos & Parts	9.60	566,000	5,434,000
Packing House Products	9.40	140,000	1,316,000
Total Exports		2,398,000	$17,577,000
Average	$8.10		
GRAND TOTAL		3,678,000	$32,973,000
% of total exports studied, moved via rail	$\frac{2,398,000}{5,016,000} \times 100 =$		47.8%

Railroads: The preceding table lists the commodities studied, the present rail rates for the routes used in the I. D. report, tonnages which would be lost to the railroads and the total loss in revenue. Tables were prepared in the same manner as described previously.

TABLE XLVII

STUDIED AND UNSTUDIED
Average

Imports	Rate Per Ton	Tonnage Lost	Loss
Studied	—	1,280,000	$15,396,000
All others (5,798,000 x 45.5%)	$8.33	2,638,000	21,975,000
Total Imports		3,918,000	$37,371,000
Exports			
Studied	—	2,398,000	$17,577,000
All Others (6,191,200 x 47.8%)	$8.10	2,959,000	23,968,000
Total Exports................................		5,357,000	41,545,000
GRAND TOTAL...................		9,275,000	$78,916,000
After deducting 42% for closed season		5,380,000	$45,772,000

The above tables show that, on a twelve months basis, the railroads would lose 9,275,000 tons to the St. Lawrence seaway if the I. D. forecasts should become manifest. This is equivalent to $78,916,000 which, when corrected for the closed season on the St. Lawrence, is equal to an annual loss of $45,772,000.

Inland Waterways: The following tables indicate the damage to existing United States inland waterways based upon the tonnages and routes represented in the I. D. Report. The rates used in these tables are the present rates in effect.

TABLE XLVIII

Loss to Water on Studied Commodities Based on Tonnages Used in I. D. Report and Present Rates

STUDIED

Imports	Rate Per Ton	Tonnage Lost	Loss
Bananas (rail loss)................................	—	—	—
Sugar, Chicago....................................	*$8.50	630,000	$5,355,000
Sugar, Minneapolis................................	*11.30	625,000	7,062,000
Coffee	6.90	280,000	1,932,000
Clay (rail losses)	—	—	—
Rubber (rail losses)	—	—	—
Total Imports		1,535,000	$14,349,000
Average.......................................	$8.90		
% of total imports studied moved by water	1,535,000 / 2,815,000	× 100 =	54.5%
* Includes Handling Charges			

Continued on next page.

TABLE XLVIII—Continued

Exports	Rate Per Ton	Tonnage Lost	Loss
Grain, Duluth	$2.18	2,618,000	$5,707,000
Flour and Meal (rail loss)	—	—	—
Iron and Steel (rail loss)	—	—	—
Agricultural Implements (rail loss)	—	—	—
Autos and Parts (rail loss)	—	—	—
Packing House Products (rail loss)	—	—	—
Total Exports		2,618,000	$5,707,000
Average	$2.18		
% of total exports studied moved by water	$\frac{2,618,000}{5,016,000}$ · 100 =		52.2%
GRAND TOTAL		4,153,000	$20,056,000

TABLE XLIX

STUDIED AND UNSTUDIED

Imports	Average Rate Per Ton	Tonnage Lost	Loss
Studied	—	1,535,000	$14,349,000
All Others (5,798,000 x 54.5%)	$8.90	3,160,000	28,124,000
Total Imports		4,695,000	$42,473,000
Exports			
Studied		2,618,000	5,707,000
All Others (6,191,200 x 52.2%)	$2.18	3,232,000	$ 7,045,000
Total Exports		5,850,000	$12,752,000
GRAND TOTAL		10,545,000	$55,225,000
After Deducting 42% for closed season		6,116,000	$32,030,000

The above tables show that should tonnage be diverted from United States inland waterways to the St. Lawrence seaway, in amounts indicated in the I. D. report, a loss of 10,545,000 tons (based on a twelve-month period) would accrue annually. This is equivalent to $55,225,000. Corrected for the closed season, the diverted tonnage would amount to 6,116,000 tons representing an annual loss of $32,030,000 to present inland waterways.

Combined Losses

Based on a twelve months period, the combined rail and inland waterway loss would be equivalent to 19,820,000 tons and $134,141,000 revenue. Corrected for the closed season, the loss in tonnage is equal to 11,489,000; the loss in revenue is equal to $77,802,000 annually.

Loss to American Ocean Shipping Based on I. D. Tonnages

The loss to American owners of ocean ships, predicated on the I. D. report's estimates of tonnage, would be greater than the losses previously derived from the Niagara Frontier Planning Board's tonnage estimate. The following tables set up the losses on studied and unstudied commodities, based on the I. D. report's tonnage, and shows the annual loss to United States ocean shipping interests based on the same system of computation described in the paragraph entitled, "Loss to American Ocean Shipping Based on Niagara Frontier Planning Board's Tonnage Estimates."

TABLE L

Yearly Loss to American Vessel-Owners on Studied Commodities
Based on Estimated Tonnages in I. D. Report

IMPORTS	PER TON LOSS	TONNAGES	LOSS
Bananas	—	740,000	—
Sugar, Chicago	$2.00	630,000	$1,260,000
Sugar, Minneapolis	2.00	625,000	1,250,000
Coffee	7.63	280,000	2,136,000
Kaolin	4.20	140,000	588,000
Rubber	18.00	400,00	7,200,000
Total		2,815,000	$12,434,000
Average	$5.64		
EXPORTS			
Grain	$1.94	2,618,000	$5,079,000
Flour & Meal	3.40	859,000	2,921,000
Iron and Steel	4.00	635,000	2,540,000
Agricultural Implements	5.00	198,000	990,000
Autos and Parts	4.40	566,000	2,490,000
Packing House Products	7.00	140,000	980,000
Total		5,016,000	$15,000,000
Average	$4.29		

TABLE LI

Yearly Loss to American Vessel-Owners on Studied and Unstudied Commodities
Based on Estimated Tonnages in I. D. Report

IMPORTS	AVERAGE PER TON LOSS	TONNAGE	LOSS
Studied	—	2,815,000	$12,434,000
All Others	$5.64	5,798,500	32,704,000
Total		8,613,500	$45,138,000
EXPORTS			
Studied	—	5,016,000	$15,000,000
All Others	$4.29	6,191,200	26,560,000
Total	11,207,200		$41,560,000
GRAND TOTAL		19,820,700	$86,698,000

It is seen that the annual damage to American ocean vessel operators, predicated on a twelve-month basis, is equivalent to $86,698,000. After deducting 42% for the closed season, 65% to correct for tonnage now carried from north American ports in foreign vessels and 45% to adjust the figure in order to make allowances for American vessels which might use the St. Lawrence seaway, this figure is reduced to an annual loss of $9,680,000.

Loss to United States Coal Industries Based on I. D. Tonnage

The loss to United States coal industries would be more when based on the I. D. tonnage estimates than when based on the Niagara Frontier Planning Board's tonnage estimates. The reason for this is that there would be a greater amount of backhaul available for coal because of the larger volume in grain export as estimated by the I. D. report.

According to the I. D. findings, the total grain exports from the United States would amount to 2,618,000 tons. When the Canadian grain exports are added to this, the total becomes 8,618,000 tons. Allowing for the closed navigation season, the figure of approximately 5,000,000 tons in export of grain from the United States and Canada is obtained. This total, of course, is based partially on the I. D. report. It has already been pointed out that most of this grain will bring a return in ballast coal shipments from Europe (see page 78). The loss to American coal interests at $3.50 per ton would approximate $17,500,000 if the I. D. report's estimates on United States grain export were reflected in coal imports from Europe.

Possible Savings Based on I. D. Tonnage and Routes
Using Present Rates

Before a net loss to American transportation systems and affiliated industries can be determined on the I. D. report's estimated tonnage movements, it is necessary to make an estimate of probable savings of a St. Lawrence seaway route over current routes. It should be understood that these are not the savings which the Niagara Frontier Planning Board believes will occur (see pages 49 and 82) but are savings based on totals given in the I. D. report. It has already been shown that the Government economists did not base their savings figures on the cheapest existing routes.

Possible Per Ton Savings: In determining the savings, a table showing the route, present cost, constructed rates via the St. Lawrence seaway and indicated savings was prepared for both studied imports and exports. The constructed rates by way of the St. Lawrence seaway are those heretofore derived in discussions pertaining to the particular commodity studied (see pages 52 to 71). The following table shows these various rates and indicated savings:

TABLE LII

Commodity	Route			Present Cost Per Ton				Constructed Rate via St. Lawrence	Indicated Savings Per Ton
	Origin	Ocean Port	Destination	Vessel	Inland Water	Rail	Total		

IMPORTS

Via I. D. Routes and Present Rate

Commodity	Origin	Ocean Port	Destination	Vessel	Inland Water	Rail	Total	Constructed Rate via St. Lawrence	Indicated Savings Per Ton
Bananas.......	Belize, Central America	N. Orleans	Chicago	$4.55	–	$17.40	$21.95	$24.10	none
Sugar, Chicago..	Havana, Cuba	" "	" "	0.99	$8.50*	–	9.49	6.24	$3.25
Sugar, Minn....	"	"	Minneapolis	0.99	11.30*	–	12.29	9.40	2.89
Coffee.........	Rio de Janeiro	"	Chicago	7.63	6.90*	–	14.53	9.86	4.67
Rubber........	Straits Settlements	New York	Akron	18.00	–	8.60	26.60	21.75	4.85
Kaolin	Liverpool	Phila.	Cincinnati	4.20	–	6.80	11.00	9.28	1.72
Average per ton									$2.90

EXPORTS

Commodity	Origin	Ocean Port	Destination	Vessel	Inland Water	Rail	Total	Constructed Rate via St. Lawrence	Indicated Savings Per Ton
Grain.........	Duluth	Montreal	Liverpool	2.07	2.01	–	4.08*	3.05	1.03
Flour & Meal	Minn.	New York	"	3.40	–	7.60	11.00	6.99	4.01
Iron & Steel	Chicago	" "	Rio de Janeiro	4.50	–	7.48	11.98	5.63	6.35
Agric. Impl.	"	" "	Liverpool	5.00	–	9.00	14.00	6.42	7.58
Autos & Parts...	Detroit	" "	"	4.40	–	9.60	14.00	4.88	9.12
Pack. Hse. Prod.	Chicago	" "	"	7.00	–	9.40	16.40	9.15	7.25
Average per ton									$5.89

*Includes handling

TABLE LIII

*Savings Based on Studied Tonnages and Routes Used in I. D. Report
and on Present Constructed Rates*

STUDIED COMMODITIES

Imports	Savings Per Ton	Tonnage	Total Savings
Bananas....................................	no saving	740,000	—
Sugar, Chicago.............................	$3.25	630,000	$2,048,000
Sugar, Minneapolis.........................	2.89	625,000	1,806,000
Coffee.....................................	4.67	280,000	1,308,000
Kaolin.....................................	1.72	140,000	241,000
Rubber....................................	4.85	400,000	1,940,000
Total Imports..............................		2,815,000	$7,343,000
Average....................................	$2.90		
Exports			
Grain, Duluth..............................	$1.03	2,618,000	$2,697,000
Flour & Meal..............................	4.01	859,000	3,445,000
Iron & Steel...............................	6.35	635,000	4,032,000
Agricultural Implements....................	7.58	198,000	1,501,000
Autos and Parts...........................	9.12	566,000	5,162,000
Packing House Products....................	7.25	140,000	1,015,000
Total Exports..............................		5,016,000	$17,852,000
Average....................................	$5.89		

The above table demonstrates that the average saving per ton of imports is $2.90 and the average saving for exports is $5.89. By applying those average savings to the unstudied commodities, the estimated savings for those commodities were determined. These, along with the studied tonnage savings, are shown in the following table.

Savings Based on Studied Commodities

The preceding table lists the studied imports and exports; the savings per ton via the proposed St. Lawrence seaway, based upon I. D. shipping routes and actual rates along those routes; the tonnage and the total savings.

TABLE LIV

*Savings Based on Studied and Unstudied Tonnages and Routes
Used in I. D. Report and Present Rates*

IMPORTS	AVERAGE PER TON SAVING	TONNAGE	SAVING
Studied................................	—	2,815,000	$7,343,000
All Others	$2.90	5,798,500	16,816,000
Total Imports.........................		8,613,500	$24,159,000
EXPORTS			
Studied................................	—	5,016,000	$17,852,000
All Others.............................	$5.89	6,191,000	36,465,000
Total Exports.........................		11,207,200	$54,317,000
GRAND TOTAL.......................		19,820,700	78,476,000
Corrected for closed season................		11,496,000	$45,516,000

Thus we find that the total savings on imports is $24,159,000; the total on exports $54,317,000 or a total on imports and exports of $78,476,000. These savings, however, are predicated on a 12-month basis and therefore must be corrected for the closed season of navigation, equivalent to a reduction of 42%. When this factor is taken into consideration, the net savings will amount to $45,516,000.

TABLE LV

*Summary of Losses Based on I. D. Report's Estimated
Use of the St. Lawrence Seaway*

The table below sets up the annual losses based upon the I. D. report's estimate of tonnage:

Annual costs, interest & maintenance (derived previously in this report)	$12,464,000
Loss to the United States Inland Transportation Systems (derivation based on I. D. tonnages)...	77,802,000
Loss to United States Ocean Carriers (see discussion based on I. D. tonnages)...	9,680,000
Loss through Diversion of Canadian Grain from United States routes and Ocean Carriers (see discussion, "Loss to United States Transportation Systems Through Diversion of Canadian Grain")..............................	4,665,000
Loss to United States Coal Industry Resulting from Foreign Competition (see discussion, "Loss to United States Coal Industries Based on I. D. Tonnage")..	17,500,000
Total..	$122,111,000
Less probable savings..	45,516,000
Annual Net Loss...	$ 76,595,000

Effect on Coastwise Shipping

The theory has been advanced that very noticeable savings will be brought about in coastwise shipping. This statement is inaccurate. Studies of several commodities could be discussed; however, in this instance one will suffice.

Before considering the comparison in actual rates, it is interesting to note the following facts in regard to typical ocean-going steamers vs. inland motor ships:

A typical steamer will carry 215% (approximately 2 1-7 times) the tonnage of a motor ship, but the typical vessel costs 350% (approximately 3 1-2 times) as much as a motor ship, and costs 150% (1 1-2 times) more to operate. The trip from Chicago to New York, via the St. Lawrence, would take approximately 71% more time than via existing routes.

While these facts were not used directly in deriving the rates below, they are the fundamental reason why the St. Lawrence seaway route would be of little value in coastwise or intercoastal shipping.

The following table will establish the economic unsoundness of coastwise trade using the St. Lawrence over present existing routes.

TABLE LVI
Canned Goods

Present ocean rate: New York City to San Francisco . . . . $11.60 per ton
Time—New York City to San Francisco via Panama Canal . . . . 526 hours

$$\text{Rate per ton-hour} = \frac{11.60}{526} = \$0.0221$$

Time—Chicago to New York City via St. Lawrence seaway . . . . 218 hours
281 hours x $0.0221 per ton-hour = $6.21 per ton

Via the St. Lawrence
    Chicago to New York via St. Lawrence . . . . $6.21 per ton
    New York to San Francisco (above) . . . . 11.60 ” ”

    Total—Chicago to San Francisco . . . . $17.81 ” ”

Via Present Routes
    Chicago to New York via present routes (motorship) . . . . $5.00 per ton
    New York to San Francisco (above) . . . . 11.60 ” ”

    Total—Chicago to San Francisco . . . . $16.60 ” ”

From this, it can be seen that the present Chicago-San Francisco route is $1.21 per ton cheaper than over the St. Lawrence.

Similar inquiries into many other commodities which might be transported to coast ports have brought the conclusion that it is more economical to send most cargoes for such destinations on New York State Barge Canal motorships rather than through the proposed St. Lawrence seaway. A few commodities, such as California lumber which is too bulky to be handled efficiently in motorships, indicate a saving. However, the importance of such tonnage is negligible.

Shipping Distances

The accompanying map, illustrating distances over present routes and over the proposed seaway, demonstrates why the St. Lawrence would not be a profitable medium for United States coastwise or inter-coastal trade. A shipper who wishes to send goods from the Great Lakes region to the coast (or vice-versa) can do so more cheaply by using such a route as the New York State Barge Canal, because the line of commerce through the St. Lawrence River is too long if the destination lies in the United States.

Let it be assumed, for instance, that a shipment is to move by water from San Francisco to Chicago. If the cargo goes to New York City and is then transferred to motor ship for the balance of the voyage through the Barge Canal and the Great Lakes, the distance would be 7399 miles. But if the ship proceeds up to the Gulf of St. Lawrence and then through the Seaway to Chicago, the distance would be 8650 miles. This difference of 1251 miles is sufficiently great to make the former trip, even although it involves a transfer charge, the more economical.

A similar situation may apply to the use of other inland water routes, like the Mississippi Valley and connecting waterways, rather than of the St. Lawrence. The geographical relationship between the proposed seaway and United States ports gives present established transportation lines the advantage.

American Vessels Could not Participate in Direct Canadian Grain Export

Canadian grain in export to the United Kingdom would comprise the vast preponderance of tonnage moving over the seaway. American interests would lose the business of handling that grain through American ports and transportation systems. This loss would not be compensated, however, by entrance of American ships into the carrying of Canadian grain to the United Kingdom, for British shipping rules prevent foreign vessels from such activity. Great Britain does not permit ships of United States registry to clear with cargoes from one British port directly to another British port. This is a universal shipping practice designed to protect each country's own merchant marine.

Thus it would not be possible for American vessels to carry Canadian grain from a Dominion port at the head of the Great Lakes to England. But British vessels, on the other hand, could handle American grain from Duluth or Chicago to the United Kingdom. Coupled with the lower operation costs of British merchant ships, which result from different labor standards, this would give the foreign vessel-owners a great advantage over Americans who wished to use the St. Lawrence.

The effect would be to defeat the efforts of the United States government in building up the American merchant marine. The seaway would represent

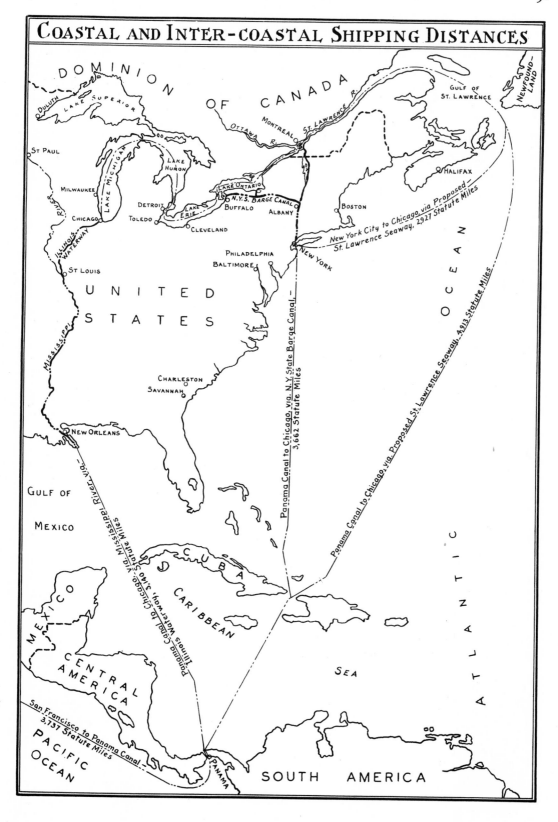

COASTAL AND INTER-COASTAL SHIPPING DISTANCES

a huge American investment resulting in diversion of business from American transportation systems to those of alien flags.

Summary of Probable Losses

The figure of $42,233,000, which represents the annual net loss to commerce and industry in the United States if the seaway were built, is the sum reached by the Niagara Frontier Planning Board after the Government's Interdepartmental Report findings had been properly adjusted. When the government's figures were studied, it was found that the estimates on the volume of traffic which might use the St. Lawrence route were greatly exaggerated. Nevertheless, the Planning Board believed that it would be interesting to determine the amount of net loss on the basis of the Interdepartmental Report's tonnage aggregates and selected routes.

The Planning Board, therefore, derived savings and loss statistics insofar as they affect American railroads, inland waterways, ocean-going vessel-owners and coal industries. Including the original cost of the proposed St. Lawrence development, the figures showed that a net annual loss of $76,595,000 would result if the government's tonnage estimates were realized. This sum is the difference between $122,111,000 in losses and $45,516,000 in savings.

Advocates of the proposed seaway have contended that it would permit a considerable savings in coastwise shipping costs. Such is not the case, because present rates over the New York State Barge Canal give that route an advantage over the St. Lawrence for coastwise trade.

The annual savings of $8,822,000, which have been derived by a comparison of transportation costs over the St. Lawrence route as against costs over present routes, are not net savings. If the seaway were constructed, the traffic which would move over it, of course, would consist of tonnage which had been diverted from present lines of commerce.

Currently established transportation interests would lose while vessel-owners using the new St. Lawrence medium would gain. It has already been pointed out, however, that the vast preponderance of the gainers would be foreign operators. Thus the seaway would result in transferring business from domestic to foreign enterprises.

There are additional indirect losses which must also be considered. Among interests in the United States, the coal operators, for instance, would be damaged by the flooding of Canadian markets with cheap foreign coal brought in from Europe as ballast cargoes.

This Canadian market is now served by American coal producers, so the proposed seaway would result in eliminating much of that market as a source of revenue for domestic mining enterprises.

When all losses are totalled, the aggregate is found to be $51,055,000 a year. The annual net loss, consequently, is $42,233,000, or the difference between the $51,055,000 in losses and the $8,822,000 in savings.

THE INCIDENTAL POWER PROJECT

ᚚ ᚚ ᚚ

St. Lawrence Power

IT is believed the foregoing sections of this report have conclusively proved that the St. Lawrence seaway canalization plan (as distinguished from the hydro-electric power portion of the plan) would create a disastrous economic hazard for existing transportation facilities in the United States.

The next point of consideration, in analyzing the St. Lawrence Seaway and Power Project as a whole, is the proposal to generate hydro-electric energy in the International Rapids Section, with possible further power development at Niagara Falls. Advocates of the St. Lawrence Seaway and New York State Power Project have contended that vast benefits of cheaper electricity would accrue to the State of New York. If it were impossible to construct the power works without the navigation works, and if the probable power benefits, to the State of New York, outweighed the inevitable seaway detriments to the State of New York and the rest of the United States, then there might be some justification for the combined seaway and power project as now envisioned by its proponents.

The Niagara Frontier Planning Board has analyzed the proposed power plans to ascertain whether these conditions, which might justify the entire scheme, have any foundation in fact.

Since it would be necessary to construct damsin the St. Lawrence River, if navigable depths were to be obtained, it has been contended that it would be possible to utilize the drop between water surfaces for the production of electrical energy. Therefore, the proponents of the seaway argue that approval of such a project not only would create an outlet to the sea for Great Lakes commerce, but would also make available considerable quantities of hydro-electric power for New York State.

It must be emphasized that the Niagara Frontier Planning Board is not opposed to advantageous development of any existing natural power resources for the State of New York. The Board does contend, nevertheless, that in order to be economically sound, such development should proceed in step with, rather than far in advance of, growing demand in the State; further, that when the same results can be obtained by one of two plans which materially differ in cost, then the cheaper program should be adopted.

Resume of the Project: As has been brought out under the heading, "International Rapids Section," the proposed power development would consist of a dam at Barnhart Island with separate American and Canadian power houses. Each power house would have 22 main units, and every unit would be capable of developing from 45,000 horsepower, under a winter head of 75 feet, to 54,400 horsepower, under a summer head of 85 feet. The head in the St. Lawrence River available for power develolpment is not constant because the level of Lake Ontario changes and because winter ice in the St. Lawrence resists the flow of water. On account of this resistance, a greater difference in elevation of water surfaces would be required above the dam to enable the river to discharge its flow. The same condition applies below the dam. At that point, the water level rises in order to force the flow under the ice sheets to Montreal and downstream. Therefore the combination of lower pond level above the dam and higher tailwater below the dam reduces the head in winter by some 10 feet.

Estimates of Cost: This report has previously presented estimates of cost of various works contemplated in the St. Lawrence River and interconnecting channels. The costs for power development in the International Rapids Section are given in detail in a section entitled, "Costs of International Rapids Section Segregated into Works Common to Navigation and Power, Works Primarily for Power, and Works Primarily for Navigation." These costs are recapitulated in the following table:

TABLE LVII

DESCRIPTION	UNITED STATES	CANADA	TOTAL
Works Common to Navigation & Power.........	$89,424,000	$18,000,000	$107,424,000
Works Primarily for Power....................	74,120,000	32,140,000	106,260,000
Works Primarily for Navigation...............	22,159,000		22,159,000
Total..	185,703,000	50,140,000	235,843,000
Contingencies (12½%)..........................	23,213,000	6,267,000	29,480,000
	208,916,000	56,407,000	265,323,000
Interest during Construction ($12\% = \dfrac{8}{2} \times 3\%$)..	25,070,000	6,769,000	31,839,000
Total Cost....................................	233,986,000	63,176,000	297,162,000
Less Amount to be Paid by New York State Power Authority (see following)....................	90,000,000		
Federal Cost.................................	$143,986,000		

The St. Lawrence Power Development Commission (created in 1930, by an act of the New York State Legislature) studied and reported on the possibilities of St. Lawrence power generation and distribution in the State of New York. The plan of development in the International Rapids Section proposed by the Commission was similar to the Joint Board of Engineers plan in that they recommended a single stage development with a power dam located in the vicinity of Barnhart Island.

If the above table is analyzed for "Works Common to Navigation and Power," together with "Works Primarily for Power," then a comparison can be made between the cost of power development under the plan proposed by the International Joint Board of Engineers and under that of the St. Lawrence Power Development Commission of the State of New York.

The following table establishes the costs of works necessary for power development alone.

TABLE LVIII

Description	United States	Canada	Total
Works Common to Navigation and Power.......	$89,424,000	$18,000,000	$107,424,000
Works Primarily for Power...................	74,120,000	32,140,000	106,260,000
Total................................	$163,544,000	$50,140,000	$213,684,000
Contingencies (12½%).....................	20,443,000	6,267,000	26,710,000
Interest during Construction ($12\% = \frac{8}{2}$ yrs. x3%)	$183,987,000 22,078,000	$56,407,000 6,769,000	$240,394,000 28,847,000
Total Cost...............................	$206,065,000	$63,176,000	$269,241,000
Less Amount to be Paid by New York State Power Authority...............................	90,000,000		
Federal Cost.............................	$116,065,000		

From the above it is evident that, should the Joint Board of Engineers plan be adopted, then the costs to the United States (including the New York State Power Authority contribution) would exceed three times the cost to Canada for an equal amount of power.

It is an interesting corollary that the St. Lawrence Power Development Commission had advanced a plan whereby the same amount of power could be developed at an estimated cost of $180,000,000 with provisions for future incorporation of the seaway features. If the costs of such development were prorated on the basis of power return, then eastern Canada and the State of New York would each pay $90,000,000, or an amount equivalent to that which is contemplated as the New York State Power Authority's share.

The Power Authority of the State of New York and the United States Engineers, subsequent to signing the treaty of 1932, reached an agreement as to the amount that the Power Authority should pay to the Federal Government in order to acquire, for the state of New York, the United States share of the International Rapids Section power rights. The amount determined was $89,726,000. For ease in determining various costs in this report, this figure has been rounded to $90,000,000. This agreement was predicated on the two stage development under consideration at that time, and presumably, this figure is subject to revision, should a single stage plan be adopted. It is not likely, however, that the figure would differ materially from $90,000,000, which represents one-half of the cost of developing the International Rapids Section for power in accordance with the plan proposed by New York State's own Power Development Commission. The original agreement called for payment by the Power Authority of:

1. $23,500,000 as its share of works common to navigation and power.
2. $29,295,500 for power house substructures, power channels, etc.
3. $36,930,500 for power house superstructures, installation of equipment etc.

Head Available for Power: The normal elevation of the proposed pond level during ice-free months would vary between 240 and 244 feet, depending on the level of Lake Ontario, and the elevation of the water in the river below the dam would be about 157. Consequently, it can be seen that the difference in elevation (or head) which might be utilized at this time for power development would be approximately 85 feet. Under winter operating conditions this head would be reduced some 10 feet because of the steeper slope in the fore-bay (estimated at 6 feet) as well as the higher elevation of the tail water (estimated at 4 feet). See "Resume of the Project" on page 94.

Flow of River: The present minimum flow of the river is 170,000 cubic feet of water per second. Under a proposed regulation of flow, the St. Lawrence Power Development Commission estimates that the minimum would be 200,000 cubic feet per second, and the average over 220,000 cubic feet per second.

Classes of Power: There are two classes of power normally considered in projects of this type, namely, "primary" and "secondary." Primary power, also referred to as "firm" power, is that power which can be relied upon at any hour, any time of the year. Secondary power is that power which is available only at certain times or under certain specific conditions such as in times of high water. This latter class is also spoken of as "irregular" power.

Horsepower Available: The St. Lawrence Power Development Commission of the State of New York reported on a single stage development operating under a head averaging 85 feet and giving 2,200,000 maximum horsepower (approximately the identical operating conditions and developed horsepower as recommended by the Joint Board of Engineers). The Commission states that, with the present minimum flow of 170,000 cfs, 1,250,000 primary horse-power could be generated. This Commission also reported that with regulated flow, the primary horsepower would be equivalent to 1,440,000, and that nor-mal secondary power would vary between 600,000 and 700,000 horsepower. It was further estimated that the average developed over a year would approxi-mate 1,900,000 horsepower.

As a result, it can be seen that the frequently quoted 2,200,000 horsepower does not represent energy available for use at all times. The energy which could be relied upon from the St. Lawrence development, unless additional steam plants were constructed as an adjunct to the hydro-electric plant to take up the slack, would be only 1,440,000 horsepower. According to the terms of the treaty, any power available would be divided equally between Canada and the United States.

Cost per Horsepower: In determining the cost per horsepower, the $90,-000,000 item based on the agreement between the Power Authority and the United States Engineers has been used. It is very probable, however, that should the project proceed, the costs would exceed this figure because of con-tingencies and of the fact that costs of generating equipment have increased considerably since 1926 when the original estimates were made. Neglecting these factors, however, and using the agreed figure, one finds that the cost per average horsepower is $94.74 and per firm horsepower $125.00.

Electrical Energy: Inasmuch as electrical energy is marketed in kilowatt-hours rather than in horsepower, the following table, based on horsepower available, has been prepared to show horsepower, equivalent kilowatts and kilowatt-hours.

TABLE LIX

Output of International Rapids Section

ITEMS	Total Horsepower	N. Y. State Horsepower	N. Y. State Kilowatts	N. Y. State Kilowatt-hours per year
Maximum capacity...........	2,200,000	1,100,000	820,000	
Average capacity.............	1,900,000	950,000	710,000	6,250,000,000
Firm capacity...............	1,440,000	720,000	540,000	4,750,000,000
Surplus or irregular power (difference)				1,500,000,000

New York's share of surplus or "irregular" power would therefore be 1,500,000,000 KWH

Load Factor: Before proceeding further with an analysis as to projected savings of St. Lawrence power over other sources, it is necessary to have an understanding of the effects of varying loads ("load factor").

If all power which could be generated at all times in a plant could be sold, then an ideal condition would exist. In practice this condition can never be obtained as it would require the consumer to vary his demand in accordance with possible power production. What actually happens is that the consumers vary their demand to fit their needs and this constant variation has to be met through amount of power generated.

As an illustration: a single domestic user often requires momentarily, or for short periods, ten times more power than his average demand. If a group of domestic consumers is considered (rather than one individual consumer) it is found that such a group will, at times, require a little more than three times their average demand. Experience shows that normally each individual peak does not tend to occur at the exact moment of other individual peaks, and hence the demand curve is somewhat "smoothed out." Diversified factories and industries have a demand somewhat over twice their average consumption.

If the average power used by a consumer (or a group of consumers), taken over a period of time, is divided by the greatest power consumption at any one interval during that period, a factor is then obtained which is commonly called "load factor".

Effect of Load Factor on St. Lawrence Power: When a hydro-electric plant is unable to store, for future use, waters not needed for power generation, great losses are occasioned by low load factors. This is the case with the proposed St. Lawrence development. During periods of low demand for power, water which is not needed for power generation must be wasted in order to maintain navigation. The result is a waste of possible power, and naturally this waste results in a greater cost, per unit, of the power actually developed. Although St. Lawrence power would, of course, not be used for domestic service alone, for purposes of discussion this assumption will be made in order to create an example and thus clarify the theory of wastage. As previously cited, aggregate domestic consumption has a load factor of approximately 30%. The St. Lawrence development would, as a whole, have an average capacity of 12½ billion KWH per year, i.e. twice the average New York share (Table LIX). The greatest number of domestic consumers that it can serve, however, would be that number whose maximum demand, at any one time, would be 9½ billion KWH. (twice the firm New York share, Table LIX). A greater demand could not be served during periods of low river flow, and hence, inasmuch as the system must be ready to serve at any hour of the day, 365 days of the year, the 9½ billion becomes the greatest safe load which can be figured for the system. Applying the 30% load factor, in accordance with the principle outlined under "Load Factor," it can readily be seen that the total yearly sales would be only 30% of 9,500,000,000, or 2,850,000,000 KWH. The cost of generating power for domestic users only would therefore be out of the question economically, because the cost of generating these 2,850,000,000 kilowatt hours would be practically the same as the cost of generating the potential 12,500, 000,000 kilowatt hours.

Wholesale Cost of St. Lawrence Power

Before the wholesale cost of power can be determined, the annual cost of operating the St. Lawrence development must be approximated. The St. Lawrence Power Development Commission, in its report, estimated that interest on the investment would amount to 4½%. This amount is believed to be low because bonds which would be sold by the Power Authority of the State of New York, to cover construction costs, would be backed neither by the credit of the State of New York nor by the real property involved; the bonds would be merely revenue bonds backed only by the contracts with private utilities for purchase of the proposed power. However, the figure was adhered to in determining the wholesale cost of power. An additional 1.87% was included for amortization and renewal.

If tax free public power is to be distributed statewide as proposed, then a fair cost can only be determined by taking into consideration the tax item. If this factor is ignored, a false picture is presented, inasmuch as any savings, appearing on the power bill because of tax exemption, would later appear in a like amount as additional levies on the tax bill. Taking a hypothetical example, let us assume that a city is now served by a public utilities company, which through its real property and franchise taxes contributes to the running expenses of the metropolis. These running expenses are the same irrespective of the source from which the revenue is obtained, and it is easily seen that if revenue from the public utilities company is foregone, then it is necessary to make up the difference by increased levies on all other real estate. While it may be argued that in a publicly-owned utility the strictly "profit item," as such, is eliminated, nevertheless interest and retirement of bonds or other fixed obligations (essentially the "profit" on a privately-owned utility) must still be provided for. What is cited in this example as applying to a city, applies with equal strength to the larger "municipality" of the State. If the use of St. Lawrence power is segregated to certain definite areas, rather than to the State at large, then the whole situation obviously becomes more unfair.

In determining the wholesale cost of power, an equivalent tax item of 1½% per cent has therefore been includeed. Thus, a fixed annual cost of 7.87% has been evolved. This, applied to the $90,000,000 estimated cost, equals $7,083,000. To the fixed cost must be added the expense of operation, estimated at $660,000, making a total annual cost of $7,743,000. This establishes the total annual cost as 1.63 mills per firm KWH, or 1.24 mills per average KWH, at the generating plant on a 100% load factor.

It was pointed out previously that approximately 1,500,000,000 KWH of surplus, irregular power would be capable of development at the International Rapids Section. Inasmuch as this power is unreliable, unless firmed up by additional steam plants, it must be dumped on the market for whatever price can be obtained at the time this surplus power is available. It is estimated that this irregular power would not bring more than three-quarters of a mill per KWH. (See page 80 of the St. Lawrence Power Development Commission Report). The 1,500,000,000 irregular KWH must be reduced by at least 10%, which is the average estimated transmission loss. The output of surplus power would then amount to approximately 1,350,000,000 KWH. At three quarters of a mill, this is equivalent to an annual income of $1,012,000. This amount, deducted from the estimated annual fixed charges and operating expenses of $7,743,000, leaves $6,731,000 as the revenue which must be obtained from the sale of firm horsepower. Inasmuch as the firm horsepower is equivalent, after deduction of transmission losses, to 4,275,000,000 KWH, the cost per KWH would be 1.57 mills. This cost is based upon a 100% load factor. As pointed out in the paragraph entitled, "Effect of Load Factor," the cost per KWH would be increased as the load factor decreases. For instance, the cost over KWH at a 50% load factor would be twice the cost at 100% load factor.

Combined Generation and Transmission Costs

It has been stated by proponents of the St. Lawrence Power Project that energy could be transmitted to New York City with great savings resulting for consumers in that area. To date, the longest distance that power has been transmitted is from Boulder Dam to Los Angeles, some 280 miles. From the St. Lawrence generating stations to New York City would be approximately 330 miles. It is not held that, simply because power has not been heretofore transmitted at such a distance, this cannot be done. However, the volume of power proposed to be furnished New York City is so great that economic requirements might demand higher transmission voltages than thus far have been attempted in actual practice. Further, no method of construction has yet been devised that would guarantee freedom from mechanical troubles or from disruptions due to natural causes. Of the complex commercial and industrial life of a municipality like New York, dependable electric power is the very life-blood. If power should fail, even for a few minutes, an intensely serious situation would ensue. It must be remembered that it requires only a momentary failure of basic power supply to result in a much more lengthy disruption of service.

The use of electricity enters many fields. While the Niagara Frontier Planning Board does not wish to pose as an alarmist, it feels that cognizance should be taken of the resultant condition if drinking water pumps were stopped, sewage lift stations and treatment works put out of operation, elevators in skyscrapers made useless, the great merchandise marts made dark, and ventilation equipment in buildings, subways and vehicular tunnels rendered ineffective. In view of all this, it is doubtful whether there is a market for a large block of power in New York City which would be subject to such possible

TABLE LX

Cost of Transmission to Various Representative Areas in New York State

Place	No. of Circuits	No. of Circuit Miles	Total Cost based on $28,000 per Circuit Mile(1)	Fixed Charges & Operation & Taxes 9%(2)	Kilowatts	Kilowatt Hours in Millions	Cost per Kilowatt hr. delivered at 100% Load Factor (In Mills)
Buffalo.................	4	1000	$28,000,000	$2,520,000	240,000	2,102	1.20
Rochester	4	800	22,400,000	2,016,000	240,000	2,102	0.96
Syracuse	4	600	16,800,000	1,512,000	240,000	2,102	0.72
Albany or Binghamton....	3	600	16,800,000	1,512,000	160,000	1,402	1.08
Elmsford...............	7	2275	63,700,000	5,733,000	480,000	4,205	1.36
New York City (1 mill additional to Elmsford cost) (1)							2.36

(1) See Appendix B, page 101 of St. Lawrence Power Development Commission report.

(2) Interest.......4.5%
    Amortization ..1.0%
    Renewal......1.5%
    Operation... .0.5%
    Taxes 1.5%
         9.0%

TABLE LXI

Cost of Generation and Transmission to Various Representative Areas of New York State at Different Load Factors in Mills per Kilowatt-hour

Load Factor	.30	.40	.50	.60	.70	.80	1.00
Buffalo							
Generation............	5.23	3.92	3.14	2.62	2.24	1.96	1.57
Transmission..........	4.00	3.00	2.40	2.00	1.71	1.50	1.20
Total..............	9.23	6.92	5.54	4.62	3.95	3.46	2.77
Rochester							
Generation............	5.23	3.92	3.14	2.62	2.24	1.96	1.57
Transmission..........	3.20	2.40	1.92	1.60	1.37	1.20	0.96
Total..............	8.43	6.32	5.06	4.22	3.61	3.16	2.53
Syracuse							
Generation	5.23	3.92	3.14	2.62	2.24	1.96	1.57
Transmission..........	2.40	1.80	1.44	1.20	1.03	0.90	0.72
Total..............	7.63	5.72	4.58	3.82	3.27	2.86	2.29
Albany or Binghamton							
Generation............	5.23	3.92	3.14	2.62	2.24	1.96	1.57
Transmission..........	3.60	2.70	2.16	1.80	1.54	1.35	1.08
Total..............	8.83	6.62	5.30	4.42	3.78	3.31	2.65
New York City							
Generation............	5.23	3.92	3.14	2.62	2.24	1.96	1.57
Transmission..........	7.87	5.90	4.72	3.93	3.37	2.95	2.36
Total..............	13.10	9.82	7.86	6.55	5.61	4.91	3.93

The figures derived in the above table are for delivery to the transformer station or sub-station, and do not include distribution costs or cost of substation. The amounts of power to be delivered to the various points have been kept in agreement with figures established in the St. Lawrence Power Development Commission's Report. (Appendix B., pg. 101).

interruptions. It is not practical, at the present time, to transmit St. Lawrence power to New York City, or to consider New York City as being part of the St. Lawrence market.

Notwithstanding this conclusion, however, an anaylsis has been made of the probable cost of St. Lawrence power delivered in New York City, along with other important upstate consuming centers. The St. Lawrence Power Development Commission made a study of transmission costs to Buffalo, Rochester, Syracuse, Binghamton, Albany and New York City. (See pages 101 and 102, St. Lawrence Power Development Commission report). The transmission costs for various load factors illustrated in table LXI are those developed by the Commission on an interest rate of $4\frac{1}{2}\%$, to which an allowance of $1\frac{1}{2}\%$ for taxes is added (as previously discussed). By adding the generation and transmission costs for the various load factors, the cost per KWH delivered at various points can be estimated.

The statistics derived in table LXI are for delivery to the transformer station or substation and do not include distribution costs or cost of substation. The amounts of power to be delivered to the various points have been kept in agreement with figures established in the St. Lawrence Power Development Commission's report. (Appendix B., p. 101).

Cost per Kilowatt Hour, Steam Plant

If St. Lawrence power is compared with new steam stations having equivalent output, it is necessary, in determining the cost per kilowatt-hour from such steam stations, to allow for total installed capacities greater than the proposed St. Lawrence output.

This is because of the fact that at more or less regular intervals, certain steam units are shut down for routine inspection and maintenance. During such maintenance periods it would still be necessary to have in operation a total of units equivalent in capacity to the hydro-electric output, a condition necessitating that the station equipment be capable of carrying the load, even with some units out of operation.

In comparing costs of equivalent steam generation as they would actually exist, however, this extra allowance of capacity need not be made, because there are now steam plants scattered throughout the system which could be used to supply power during the regular maintenance periods of new stations, either steam or hydro-electric. These standby plants do not have the high efficiency rating of modern plants, and consequently their use as standby capacity units is the most practical purpose to which they can be put. In fact, many of these plants are used at the present time for this very purpose. These standby units are as essential to hydro-electric as they are to modern steam generation. In comparing costs of St. Lawrence power vs. modern steam generation, the same load factor can therefore be used in either instance.

While it is probable that the cost per kilowatt-hour would vary somewhat according to locality because of the price of coal and certain other factors, nevertheless it is felt that only three main state subdivisions need be considered to give a general comparison, namely, New York City, Central New York and Buffalo.

Cost of Steam Generation, Central New York: The most important variable entering into the cost of steam generation is the fuel cost. At the present time steam coal of a satisfactory grade costs approximately $5.00 per ton in New York City, an average of $4.00 per ton in Central New York State and $3.50 per ton at Buffalo.

In determining the probable cost per kilowatt-hour in Central New York, an investigation was made of the estimated power production costs at the steam plant now being constructed at Oswego, New York. This plant is being designed for 5 units, each having a capacity of 80,000 kilowatt gross, or 75,000 kilowatts in sendout after allowances for station services and auxiliaries are made. Two units are now under construction. It is estimated that the cost of power from these two units will vary from 4.0 mills at 80% capacity factor, to 7.5 mills at 30% capacity factor, and that upon completion of the fifth unit, the cost per KWH for 80% capacity factor will be 3.8 mills and at 30% capacity factor, 7.0 mills. These data, together with generating costs at other stations, are shown in the following table.

TABLE LXII

Estimated Cost of Steam Generated Electric Power Delivered
To Bus — Mills Per Kilowatt-hour

	Oswego—5 Units Ultimate Capacity %			Buffalo	New York
Capacity Factor %	At Completion of First Unit*	At Completion of Second Unit*	At Completion of Fifth Unit	Huntley No. 2 2 Units	See Discussion Following
30	8.8	7.5	7.0	6.0	8.3
40	7.2	6.1	5.7	4.9	6.8
50	6.1	5.2	4.9	4.3	5.9
60	5.3	4.7	4.5	3.9	5.3
70	4.9	4.3	4.0	3.6	4.8
80	4.6	4.0	3.8	3.4	4.5

*Now under construction

In order to select a fair figure for steam generation in central New York, the cost per kilowatt-hour shown in the preceding table under "Completion of Second Unit" has been used. These costs are approximately 5% higher than they will be upon completion of the fifth unit.

Cost of Steam Generation, Buffalo Area: As a yardstick in determining probable costs of future steam generation in the Buffalo area, the costs of electric power delivered to the bus bar at the Huntley No. 2 Plant have been used. This plant has 2 units, each with a capacity of 75,000 kilowatts, net sendout.

The cost per kilowatt-hour at 80% capacity factor is 3.4 mills, while at 30% capacity factor it is 6.0 mills.

Cost of Steam Generation, New York City: On page 109 of the St. Lawrence Power Development Commission report, curves are shown which are based upon a cost of $5.00 per ton for coal having a heating value of 13,800 BTUs per pound. The curve referred to estimates the cost per kilowatt-hour at 80% capacity factor as 4.5 mills, and at 30% capacity factor, 8.3 mills. This along with other estimated costs are shown in table LXII.

Value of St. Lawrence Power in New York City: It will be noted in Table LXI that the cost per kilowatt-hour of St. Lawrence power, delivered in New York City, varies from 13.1 mills at 30% load factor to 4.91 mills at an 80% load factor. Table LXII shows that equivalent steam generation could produce power in New York City for 8.3 mills per kilowatt-hour at a 30% load factor and for 4.5 mills at an 80% load factor. This further substantiates the statements made previously in this report that St. Lawrence power cannot be economically transmitted directly to New York City because steam generation would be cheaper.

Value of St. Lawrence Power in Buffalo Area: Table LXI shows that at 80% load factor, St. Lawrence power could be delivered directly to Buffalo for 3.46 mills while Table LXII shows that steam stations in Buffalo could generate power at the same capacity factor for 3.4 mills. At a 30% load factor, St. Lawrence power could be delivered for 9.23 mills while modern steam plants under the same conditions could generate power at 6.0 mills per kilowatt-hour. Similarly, steam plants located in the Buffalo area would be able to generate power at intermediate capacity factors cheaper than could St. Lawrence power be delivered in that area. Therefore, St. Lawrence power cannot compete against coal in Buffalo.

Value of St. Lawrence Power Upstate: Inasmuch as it has been shown that it would not be profitable, or practical, to transmit St. Lawrence power to New York City, or Buffalo, it would be necessary to dispose of the entire output in central upstate New York. This area may be roughly defined as extending from Rochester on the west to Albany on the east. It is, however, doubtful that this area alone would be able to assimilate such a great block of power for many years to come. That being the case, in order to dispose of the proposed output, the market would have to be extended to include the Buffalo area. As established above, any marketing of St. Lawrence power in Buffalo would be accomplished under a handicap. Since local power is cheaper, St. Lawrence rates would have to be reduced to an equal or even competitive level. In order to offset this reduction, and still maintain the total gross revenue, it would be necessary to sell St. Lawrence power in other areas at rates higher than would otherwise be necessary. Even then it is doubtful that the market could assimilate the St. Lawrence output for quite some time. This, of course, would of its own weight result in an increase of St. Lawrence rates and a consequent reduction in any savings brought about by the St. Lawrence development. The only other alternative, during the period required for the upstate New York market to assimilate this block of St. Lawrence power, would be the curtailing of output of existing privately owned hydro and steam plants. In that event, the losses which would be suffered would also reduce the effectiveness of any savings resulting from the St. Lawrence development, because the power curtailment in the private stations would result in an increase in the cost of producing private power necessary for supplying peak demands. It can be seen that under either alternative the savings to be effected through use of St. Lawrence power are subject to some reduction.

Assuming, however, that the market could immediately absorb the St. Lawrence power without the displacement of private plant production, the savings as compared with equivalent steam generation would not be as great as has been generally believed. In arriving at this conclusion, it has been assumed that 1,167,000,000 firm kilowatt-hours would be sold in each of the Buffalo, Rochester and Syracuse areas, and that 774,000,000 kilowatt-hours would be sold in the Albany area. It has been demonstrated previously that the cost of St. Lawrence power delivered at 80% load factor to these consuming areas would vary from 2.86 to 3.46 mills per kilowatt-hour. It has also been shown that equivalent steam generation would cost from 3.4 to 4.5 mills per kilowatt-hour. In the following tables, the consuming area, kilowatt-hours, cost per kilowatt-hour and total costs are shown for both St. Lawrence and equivalent steam power.

TABLE LXIII

Cost of St. Lawrence Power at Substation

	Kilowatt-hours in millions	Cost per KWH in mills at 80% Load Factor	Cost in Dollars
Buffalo	1,167	3.46	$4,037,820
Rochester	1,167	3.16	3,687,720
Syracuse	1,167	2.86	3,337,620
Albany	774	3.31	2,561,940
Total	4,275*		$13,625,100

(*St. Lawrence firm output, less 10% average transmission losses)

In comparing Table LXIII, above, with Table LX, Page 101, it will be noted that the transmission lines are designed for larger KW delivery than is anticipated for the average in each of the communities considered. This is done in order to provide flexibility in operation and to create the ability of the transmission lines to carry larger amounts of power, should the demand require it. The carrying capacity for firm power alone would have to be 166,000 KW. This figure is reached by dividing the 1,460,000,000 KWH at 100% load factor by 8,760 (the number of hours in a year). During certain periods there will be available 280,000 KW of secondary or irregular power (820,000-540,000 KW, Table LIX), and if Buffalo can absorb one-quarter of this amount, the lines should be capable of delivering it. By adding the firm power capacity (166,000 KW) to one-fourth the secondary (70,000 KW) a total carrying capacity of 236,000 KW is reached. This closely approximates the design capacity shown in Table LX.

TABLE LXIV

Cost of Steam Generation per Kilowatt-hour at Bus Bar

	Kilowatt-hours in millions	Cost per KWH in mills at 80% Load Factor	Cost in Dollars
Buffalo	1,167	3.4	$3,968,000
Rochester	1,167	4.0	4,668,000
Syracuse	1,167	4.0	4,668,000
Albany	774	4.5*	3,483,000
Total	4,275		$16,787,000

(*Same as New York City as coal prices are approximately the same)
Saving in St. Lawrence Power delivered Upstate:

Steam Cost........$16,787,000
St. Lawrence........ 13,625,000

$ 3,162,000

Niagara Falls Power

The preceding analysis as to power benefits was based on St. Lawrence power alone. The proposed treaty provides, in Article IX, that the governments, after adoption of final plans for the project in the International Rapids Section, shall make arrangements for works in the Niagara River.

Niagara Falls and the River: The Niagara River carries the vast flow of the Great Lakes system from Lake Erie to Lake Ontario. It flows over and through the Niagara escarpment which separates the two lakes. The river leaves Lake Erie at Buffalo and runs for some 36 miles in a generally northerly direction. During the first four miles, the flow is quite swift, then the river widens out and runs more slowly for 18 miles to the head of the Niagara Falls rapids. The rapids, approximately one mile in length, have a drop of some 50 feet.

The flow through the rapids is divided by Goat Island into two separate watercourses. The westerly flow discharges over the Canadian or Horseshoe Falls into the head of the Maid-of-the-Mist Pool 160 feet below. The easterly flow discharges over the American Falls and enters the lower river at the side of the Maid-of-the-Mist Pool. The river then continues its northerly flow through the Niagara Gorge which has a drop of approximately 96 feet in the 6 miles to Queenston, Ontario. The river, in this section, runs between vertical cliffs from 200 to 300 feet in height. After leaving Queenston, the river becomes wider, flowing at a moderate rate for 7 miles to its junction with Lake Ontario at Niagara-on-the-Lake.

The majestic, awe-inspiring beauty of Niagara Falls has drawn millions of visitors from all over the world. Its continuation as one of the world's natural wonders is of paramount importance to both the United States and Canada. During recent years, the spectacle has been somewhat impaired through hydro-electric power diversions and the rapid rate of erosion concentrating in the center part of the Horseshoe Falls.

On the Canadian side there are two secondary natural channels which converge their flow at the center part of the Horseshoe Falls, with a resulting concentration of water at that point. Such concentration produces an abnormal amount of erosion in this section to make what is known locally as a "notch". It reduces the amount of water clothing the two flanks of the Horseshoe Falls and also, to a great extent, lessens the scenic effectiveness of the curtain of water flowing over the American Falls.

Existing Niagara Falls Power Facilities: The first successful power development at Niagara Falls on the United States side was initiated in 1877 by the Niagara Falls Hydraulic Power and Manufacturing Company. From that time on, there have been many different developments carried on with varying success. During recent years, in the interest of efficiency, power rights have gradually been obtained by the Niagara Falls Power Company, which, at the present time, has the following installations:

TABLE LXV

Existing Plants at Niagara Falls

United States Side Station	Head	Flow	Rated H. P.	Actual H. P. at Full Gate
Schoellkopf	217	24,000	452,000	499,000
Adams	135	8,800	105,000	107,000
Total		32,800	557,000	606,000

Power development on the Canadian side began in 1893 with an installation of 2000 horsepower for the International Railway Company. This station is now inoperative. Since then, developments on the Canadian side have expanded rapidly. Most of the stations are now controlled by the Ontario Hydro-Electric Power Commission. However, there is one station owned by American interests, namely the Rankine Station. The capacities of installations on the Canadian side are shown in the following table:

TABLE LXVI

Canadian Side Station	Head	Flow	Rated H. P.	Actual H. P. at Full Gate
Rankine........................	127	10,420	121,000	103,000
Toronto........................	135	16,400	157,000	148,000
Queenston......................	305	16,000	565,000	490,000
Ontario........................	180	10,800	205,000	174,000
Total........................		53,620	1,048,000	915,000

The Rankine Station is owned by the Canadian Niagara Power Company, a subsidiary of the Niagara Falls Power Company. It is licensed to develop 100,000 horsepower, requiring 10,200 cfs. The Canadian Niagara Power Company has a contract with the Buffalo Niagara Electric Corporation for the delivery of 50,000 horsepower to that company.

Present Power Diversions: In 1909, the boundary waters treaty between Canada and the United States established the amount of diversion which could be withdrawn on either side at Niagara Falls for power purposes. Thirty-six thousand second feet was established as the diversion on the Canadian side, and 20,000 second feet on the United States side. Inasmuch as half of the output in the Rankine Station American-owned is exported to the United States and approximately 5,100 cubic feet per second is required to develop this power, the present diversions in effect are 30,900 second feet to Canada and 25,100 second feet to the United States and American subsidiary companies. In addition to the power exported to the United States from the Rankine station, there are additional quantities of power sold to United States companies by the Ontario Hydro-Electric Power Commission, a public agency.

Proposed Works

As noted above, the proposed St. Lawrence Treaty provides that certain works shall be undertaken in the Niagara River to insure unbroken crest lines on both the American and Canadian Falls as well as to permit safe and practical diversions of water for power purposes.

Special International Niagara Board: The International Niagara Board of Control, as differentiated from the Special International Niagara Board, was established in 1923, under instructions of the two governments, to supervise and control diversions of water permitted in the boundary waters treaty of 1909. The Board, in connection with this administrative responsibility, reviewed numerous earlier investigations looking to the preservation of the Falls. It was agreed by the members of this Board that its personnel should be increased from two to four and established as a Special International Niagara Board for the purpose of accomplishing these investigations. This work was aggressively carried on through 1927 and toward the end of that year had advanced sufficiently to permit the Board to reach certain conclusions. Accordingly, on December 14 of that year, an interim report was submitted to the Governments recommending the early construction of initial works which it deemed highly desirable.

Recommendations: Briefly, the Board recommended that submerged weirs be constructed above the Falls to impede the flow which concentrates at the center of the cataract. The water now discharging over the center part of the Horseshoe Falls often exceeds 10 feet in depth, whereas only 6 feet is necessary to preserve the scenic effect. The proposed obstruction would not be noticeable from the surface of the water but would divert more flow to the flanks of the Horseshoe Falls and to the American Falls. Also recommended were light excavations to be made on either side of the Horseshoe Falls to assist the submerged weirs in distributing the flow more evenly. By so doing the flow now concentrated in the center part of the Falls would be greatly reduced with consequent lessening in the rate of erosion. This plan would also, because of more practical use of the water, provide for further power development.

Of late years the actual flow over the Falls, as given by the Special International Niagara Board, has varied from approximately 90,000 to 160,000 cubic feet per second.

In the report of the Special International Niagara Board it was stated that this extra water for power use would undoubtedly be equivalent to 20,000 cubic feet per second. However, the Board did recommend that no permanent treaty permitting additional withdrawal be consummated until after the 20,000 second feet had been diverted and the effects on scenic beauty determined. If no detrimental effects were noted, permanent withdrawal might be then allowed or, if there were some detrimental effects, the permanent withdrawal might be adjusted to an amount which would not injure the scenic spectacle.

Diversion Effects on Upper and Lower Rapids: Another consideration is the problem of ice troubles in the upper and lower rapids. The Board concluded that a flow of at least 50,000 cubic feet per second in the upper rapids would be necessary to flush ice over the falls. It then estimated that an additional diversion of 20,000 second feet could be permitted without reducing the flow in the rapids below the amount necessary for this purpose.

In reporting on the effects of diversion around the lower rapids, the Board concluded that it was not possible to pre-determine any definite amounts of flow which would obviate the possibility of ice trouble. This conclusion was based upon the fact that even without any diversion around the lower rapids, ice jams have occurred. The Board pointed out, however, that a diversion of 40,000 second feet would not aggravate this condition to any alarming extent because it would only increase the duration of the normal period of low flows by 2%. The Board did report, however, that a flow of 60,000 feet would present an entirely different picture, since in that case the duration of the low flow period would be increased by 25%.

Potential Horsepower: According to the proposed treaty of 1938, an additional diversion of 5,000 second feet would be allowed both countries following construction of preservation works. If the total head available, that is 215 feet at the Falls and some 100 feet through the lower rapids, were utilized, one cubic foot of water would be equivalent to approximately 31 potential horsepower. If the head available at the Falls were utilized alone, one cubic foot would be equivalent to approximately 21 horsepower. In other words, 5,000 second feet, if developed under the full head, would represent 155,000 horsepower and under the head at Niagara Falls only, would represent 105,000 horsepower. Should the amount of diversion later be raised to 10,000 second feet on each side in accordance with the possibilities determined by the Special International Niagara Board, the total potential horsepower available on either side, of course, would be doubled.

Cost of Preservation Works: The Special International Niagara Board, in making their study of the Niagara Falls problem, made extensive estimates of cost of the project. They concluded the work could be completed for the sum of $1,750,000. During previous deliberations $750,000 was considered as the Canadian contribution and $1,000,000 as the United States' share.

Possible Development of Power: It can be seen from the preceeding discussion that there are several possibilities of utilizing the potential diversion for power purposes. Power could be generated by utilizing only the Niagara Falls head, or in plants making use of the full head of 315 feet or in a combination of plants developing first the 215 feet at the Falls but supplemented by another plant below the lower rapids using the head available in that section of the river. Inasmuch as diversion around the lower rapids presents some undesirable features because of possible ice hazards, it appears that the two-stage development would be more practical. In that instance, if difficulties arose because of too great diversion around the lower rapids, the lower plant could be wholly or partially shut down, thereby increasing the flow through the lower rapids (without reducing the normal output at the Falls plant). While no definite plan has yet been advanced for the actual mechanics of developing the so-called second step, nevertheless the basic principle is established. Water must be taken from the head of the lower rapids and conveyed either in open channels, having only a sufficient drop to cause the water to flow, or in large pipes or tunnels under pressure. Due to the fact that the river, for a distance of some 6 miles, flows between vertical cliffs, either scheme would be costly. Previous investigations disclose that it would not be economical to develop this head unless a flow of 10,000 cfs can be depended upon nearly all of the time.

The Special International Niagara Board did not formulate a definite plan with estimates of cost in connection with power to be developed at Niagara Falls. Therefore, it is impossible to evaluate Niagara Falls power, on the basis of their recommended diversions, and compare it with the cost of equivalent steam generation in the Buffalo area.

Power Authority of the State of New York

The Power Authority of the State of New York was created by an act of the State Legislature in 1931 and was authorized to develop St. Lawrence power in conjunction with the federal government, should the St. Lawrence project become an actuality. It was also authorized to make studies in connection with the coordination of that energy and other hydro-electric and steam-generated power throughout the state. However, it was not empowered to proceed with the construction of the Niagara Falls project or any other works outside the St. Lawrence area.

The Power Authority, in its annual report of 1938, recommended a coordinated system of St. Lawrence and Niagara Falls power, together with additional steam plants, transmission lines and increased capacity distribution systems. These will be briefly discussed in the following paragraphs.

The Power Authority plan for the development of Niagara Falls is considerably more extensive than the one proposed by the Special International Niagara Board. It is proposed by that agency to construct a series of gates across the Niagara River in the vicinity of Buffalo for the purpose of regulating Niagara River flows. The report suggest that, through the operation of these gates, it would be possible to reduce the flow over the falls at night and thereby store water in Lake Erie for daytime use. It is claimed that by this system of river control, the surplus water stored in Lake Erie could be used to increase power production. The Power Authority contends that by so doing an additional 6,800 second feet might be withdrawn for the United States and 6,500 second feet for Canada (from the storage of night flows) for 100% of the time, and still leave 50,000 cubic feet per second for scenic and ice sluicing purposes and 66,000 cubic feet per second for power purposes. It will be noted that in this conclusion the 6,800 and 6,500 cfs are over and above the 10,000 proposed in the tentative treaty submitted by our government to Canada in 1938.

The Power Authority plan contemplates that the additional diversion of 6,800 and 6,500 cfs, respectively, would be utilized in what is termed a stage one power development. On completion of a second stage development, it is proposed that the storage of water would be limited to the hours of darkness throughout the tourist season. The proposed use of the water was suggested as follows:

1. Minimum diversion during tourist season, 90,000 cfs, of which half would be for the United States.
2. During daylight hours of the tourist season the entire river flow over and above 100,000 cfs would be utilized.

3.   During darkness hours of the tourist season the water representing
     the difference between 100,000 cfs (daylight flow) and 50,000 cfs
     (night flow) would be stored in Lake Erie for winter use, except such
     amounts as might be necessary to maintain diversion.

4.   The Schoellkopf Power Station on the United States side would be
     shut down during the tourist season insofar as any stated flow is con-
     cerned, operating only to utilize any excess water when the natural
     flow of the river should leave more than 50,000 cfs available for
     power after deduction of 100,000 cfs for scenic purposes.

5.   During winter months, when stored water is proposed to supplement
     natural flows, the Schoellkopf station would operate with the use of
     15,000 cfs. The remaining water for power purposes (up to 50,000
     cfs) would be utilized through the full head station. Should any
     additional water be available for power up to the capacity of 24,000
     cfs, it would be utilized in the Schoellkopf plant.

All of these diversions are predicated on a tourist season flow of 100,000
cfs over the Falls and through the rapids during daylight hours, 50,000 cfs over
the Falls and through the rapids during the night hours, and a winter season
flow of 50,000 cfs day and night over the Falls, and 80,000 cfs day and night
through the rapids.

The technical ramifications of this plan are obviously tremendous. When
one attempts to regulate flows through the Niagara River, the levels of both
Lake Erie and Lake Ontario are affected. While theoretically such regulation
is possible, in actual practice it is questionable whether it can be accomplished
without causing many complications, both national and international, while
the troubles which would undoubtedly arise from ice blockades are manifold.
The danger in this was pointed out by the Joint Board of Engineers in their
report on the St. Lawrence Seaway Project.

Power Development in the Niagara River: On the basis of these diversion
assumptions, the Power Authority recommended a new full-head development
with an installed capacity of 787,500 horsepower and using 25,000 second feet.
The estimated cost of this plant, including one-half of the remedial works and
one-half the cost of regulating works, is $77,855,000. The claimed net gain in
kilowatt-hours for this first stage development is 4,509,000,000. The Authority then proposed the construction of a second full head plant to use an additional 25,000 cubic feet of water per second. This plant was to have a capacity
of 787,500 horsepower. It was estimated to cost, including necessary river
enlargements, $68,510,000.

Coordinating System: The Power Authority further proposed the coordination of St. Lawrence and Niagara Falls power with a publicly owned transmission system extending to seven points of distribution in the state; the

supplementing of St. Lawrence and Niagara Falls power plants with privately owned steam generating stations, and an increase in private distribution system capacities.

Estimated Cost: The Authority estimated the system cost, including first stage development only, as:

TABLE XLVII

To be paid Federal Government for International Rapids Section Power Plant..........	$90,000,000
Estimated cost-Niagara Falls development......	78,000,000
Super Grid System, New York State..........	105,000,000
Interest during construction.................	14,000,000
	$287,000,000

To this must be added as per report of New York State Power Authority for 1938:

Developments of private companies—	
Cost of required steam plants to carry anticipated load........................	$192,400,000
Cost of adaptation present private distribution to new system....................	119,960,000
	312,360,000

Total cost of Power Project	$599,360,000
Second Stage development at Niagara Falls.....	68,510,000
Grand total including second stage development	*$667,870,000

*This money would be raised by private companies and by Power Authority bonds, without committing the credit of the State.

Estimated Power Demand: In justification of a near $600,000,000 expenditure for power development (first stage power development at Niagara Falls only), the Authority claimed a 1950 power demand in the State of New York approximately double of that in 1937. In this latter year, the power sales in New York State were 13,495,926,000 kilowatt-hours. The Authority contends that in 1950 the demand will be 26,870,000,000 KWH. In arriving at this anticipated demand, the Power Authority developed a curve of consumption for the years 1924 to 1938 inclusive and projected this curve to 1950. This is shown in the following figure:

PLATE I

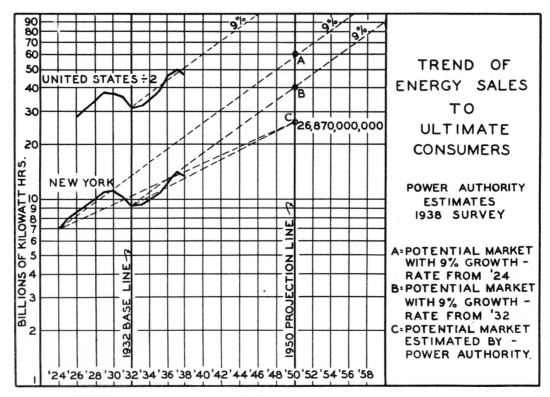

The Power Authority, in projecting the demand curve, neglected to consider the fact that business depressions are bound to occur in the future just as they have in the past and that during such depression periods power consumption falls off materially. As a result, it takes several years before the existing supply of power is once again utilized and, as a consequence, the time when additional power facilities are required is materially postponed.

In its forecast of power consumption, the Authority argued that the demand would be accentuated because of claimed reductions in consumer rates. During the period 1924-39 there was a decrease in consumer rates practically equivalent to the amount which the Power Authority states would be the future decrease over the 1939 rates. The reduction in rates between 1924 and 1939 occurred without public ownership of power generating or transmitting systems.

In the following curve, the trend of power sales from 1924 to 1939 was projected from the power sales of 1939. This, it is believed, will give a more likely forecast of the probable future demand by years. It may be argued that in this projected curve the reduction in power sales in the years 1930 to 1933 are repeated. On the other hand, however, the sharp gains in power demands between '24 and '29 are likewise repeated.

The proper curve projected from 1929 to 1952 shows that the probable demand in that year will be 21,000,000,000 KWH as compared with 26,870,-000,000 forecast by the Power Authority for the year 1950. Also shown in the plate below is a smooth curve trend extending from 1910 to 1952. This curve shows that in 1950 the anticipated demand might be 21,400,000,000 KWH, and in 1952, 22,800,000,000 KWH.

PLATE II

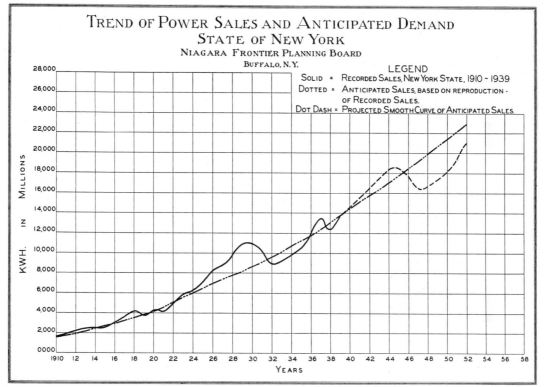

TREND OF POWER SALES AND ANTICIPATED DEMAND
STATE OF NEW YORK
NIAGARA FRONTIER PLANNING BOARD
BUFFALO, N.Y.

LEGEND
SOLID = RECORDED SALES, NEW YORK STATE, 1910 - 1939
DOTTED = ANTICIPATED SALES, BASED ON REPRODUCTION - OF RECORDED SALES.
DOT DASH = PROJECTED SMOOTH CURVE OF ANTICIPATED SALES.

Savings Claimed by Power Authority and Danger of Over-Development

In the 1939 Annual Report of the Power Authority, it is stated that should its plan of St. Lawrence and Niagara Falls development be coordinated with additional steam generating plants, through a new and vast transmission network, the annual saving over equivalent steam generation would amount to $22,000,000. However, since this plan is based upon a demand of 26,870,000,-000 KWH, any material reduction in that demand would reduce the estimated savings in like manner. For instance, the 1950 power demand as estimated by the Niagara Frontier Planning Board shows that approximately 21,000,000,000 KWH would be required as against the Power Authority's estimate of 26,870,-000,000. The difference between these two estimates is 5,870,000,000 KWH which, by coincidence, is the approximate output of the St. Lawrence development. This shows the importance of not over-developing, a point which was stressed in the St. Lawrence Power Development Commission's Report on the practicability of creating St. Lawrence power. The Commission constantly emphasizes that hydro-electric energy often is developed so far in advance of the market that it results in a financial failure because of the high fixed charges on that type of plant. The following is a direct quotation from that report (page 45):

"Usually, natural conditions will not permit of a progressive development to keep pace with a growing market. Sometimes this gives rise to the temptation to build in spite of the lack of market, in the hope that the load will grow to absorb the power. There is no more dangerous policy to pursue, for there is always the serious liability that the capital charges on the excess unemployed portion of the investment will accumulate to such magnitude that the project will not pay."

Following out this policy, the St. Lawrence Power Development Commission recommended that St. Lawrence power be developed in two steps, that is, the development of the main dam for only a portion of its height for the first step, and after the power market had absorbed the output, raising the dam to its full height so as to develop the complete potential power of the St. Lawrence.

In view of this warning, it appears that the Power Authority's recommendations are ill-advised when it urges a program involving the expenditure of nearly 600 millions of dollars to meet a power demand estimated so far in the future.

Progressive Power Development Independent of Seaway

The Niagara Frontier Planning Board has long supported the plan of the Special International Niagara Board for restoring the beauty of Niagara Falls and preventing rapid erosion there, while at the same time making available for further power development a possible addition of 10,000 cfs of water on both sides of the border. This plan has no connection with the St. Lawrence Seaway Project and it enables the following out of a progressive development of further hydro-electric power. In Table LXV it may be seen that on the American side there are existing plants which can take a flow of 32,800 second feet. The only diversion allowed on the American side at the present time is 20,000 s.f. Therefore, with the construction of the preservation works recommended by the Special International Niagara Board, an additional 10,000 s.f. could be put through present plants on the American side, which with their existing heads would create an additional 156,000 H.P., or 1,013,000,000 KWH per year. The cost to the United States for such preservation works would be only $1,000,000.

On the Canadian side, it will be noted in Table LXVI, there are plants capable of handling 53,620 cfs. The diversion permitted on the Canadian side is only now 36,000 cfs. Therefore, an additional 10,000 cfs, resulting from the preservation works, could be diverted through existing plants on the

Canadian side to develop a further 97,000 H.P. This would be equivalent to 646,190,000 KWH. The cost of the preservation works on the Canadian side to enable the development of this power would amount to only $750,000. This is, consequently, the most sensible first step in further hydro-electric power development for both Ontario and New York.

The next logical move in generating further hydro-electric energy for the State of New York would appear to be the construction of a plant utilizing the head in the lower Niagara River rapids, so that, in effect, there would be a full-head development in two steps: the first step through utilizing the head at the Falls, and the second step in developing the suitable head of the lower rapids. Such a two-step development would then be very flexible in its operation and, if ice troubles occurred in the lower rapids, the use of the second step could be curtailed to increase the flushing ability of the lower river.

All of this work could be done in accordance with the growth of power demand and absolutely independent of any seaway undertaking.

When the time for further hydro-electric development arrives, the St. Lawrence River might be developed. This also could be done independently of a seaway. Advocates of the seaway project have fathered the belief that, in order to develop power in the St. Lawrence, it is necessary for the project to be a joint seaway and power undertaking. This is entirely contrary to engineering knowledge and reports on the subject.

Upon completion of its survey, the St. Lawrence Power Development Commission of the State of New York showed that the same horsepower as proposed in the present plan could be developed for $180,000,000. If this cost were borne equally between the two countries, it would amount to $90,000,000 each. It has been reported that the Province of Ontario contemplates paying the Dominion Government some $76,000,000 for the power rights at the International Rapids Section. If this be true, then the development of Canadian power, independent of the seaway and of a United States subsidy for Canadian power, could be accomplished for only $14,000,000 more than now is contemplated by the Province of Ontario. Incidentally, development of power by this or some similar plan in the International Rapids Section would not preclude the possibility of a seaway's being constructed at some time in the future should conditions change so as to warrant it economically.

American Subsidy of Canadian Power

In order to make a strict comparison between the actual costs of power to Canada and to New York, a further breakdown of "Works Common to Power and Navigation" should be made. For purposes of discussion it has been assumed that those items which are common to both power and navigation are chargeable in equal proportions to each phase of the combined project. Based on this hypothesis, the strict Canadian power cost is as follows:

One half of "Works Common to Power and Navigation"... $9,000,000
Works Primarily for Power...............................   32,140,000

Total Canadian Cost Chargeable to Power.............. $41,140,000

Under the plan advanced by New York State's Power Development Commission (by far the least expensive one proposed), an amount of power equal to that contemplated by the seaway project was recommended for a total expenditure of $180,000,000. Of this amount, one-half, or $90,000,000 would be the Canadian share. If Canada can obtain the same results for $41,140,000 under the St. Lawrence seaway scheme as she can for $90,000,000 under the Power Development Commission's plan, it is obvious that the seaway scheme would have American dollars subsidize Canadian power to the extent of $48,860,000.

Present Power Resources in Eastern Canada

In considering the power situation in the Dominion of Canada, it is clear that Canadian economic and industrial advancement in no way requires the development of International Rapids energy. There are now available, in Canada, huge power potentialities which may be developed rapidly and economically and which are entirely divorced from any St. Lawrence seaway plan.

One striking example is the Beauharnois plant, where 1,000,000 additional horsepower could be produced by the simple expedient of installing the necessary machinery. Among other easily developed supplies of major importance are 2,900,000 horsepower on the Ottawa River and 1,160,000 horsepower on the St. Maurice.

The Hydro-Electric Power Commission of Ontario has appended to its Report of 1936 a map on which are indicated no less than 21 proposed sites for future hydro-electric power generation. None of these has any association with the St. Lawrence seaway.

As previously cited in this report, there are possibilities of additional development at Niagara Falls, where the installation of remedial works incidental to the preservation of the falls would net Canada some 96,600 additional horsepower by utilization of the Falls head alone through existing stations.

Another plan which the Province of Ontario is desirous of carrying out is the diversion of some 5000 second-feet of water into Lake Superior from Long Lake (Longue Lac) and the Ogoki, Albany and Kenogami Rivers. This would be accomplished by reversing the flow in the Kenogami River and would permit Canada to use this 5000 second-feet at Niagara Falls to develop an additional 45,100 horsepower through existing plants to make a total with the 96,600 previously mentioned of 141,700 horsepower. If the water from Long Lake (5,000 sf.) and that made available at Niagara Falls through the diversion works (10,000 sf.) were used under full head in new plants, 450,000 horsepower could be developed.

It is not the purpose of this discussion to tabulate all of the potential power supplies in the Dominion of Canada, but rather simply to establish the fact that the failure of the St. Lawrence project to become a reality would in no way impede the progress of that part of Canada which could be served by the International Rapids development.

Summary of the Incidental Power Project

According to the plan proposed by the Joint Board of Engineers for the development of power in the International Rapids Section, the total first cost for power alone would exceed $269,000,000. Of this amount, $63,000,000 would be Canada's share, and $206,000,000 the United States' share. In event the Power Authority of the State of New York paid the United States Government $90,000,000 for power rights, the federal cost in the International Rapids Section for power alone would exceed 116 millions of dollars. A large portion of this would, in effect, be for the construction of works primarily benefiting the development of Canadian power. The plan would provide for the installation of equipment having a maximum capacity of 2,200,000 horsepower. However, because of the varying flows in the river, the "firm" amount would be only 1,400,000 horsepower, half of which would be for the benefit of the State of New York.

It has been shown that transmission of St. Lawrence power directly to New York City is impractical at the present time and will continue to be so until new methods of transmission are evolved to prevent interruption of service in that metropolitan area. This fact would require the direct absorption of St. Lawrence power in the upstate area where it would be somewhat cheaper than equivalent steam generation. These savings, however, are estimated as only approximately $3,000,000 per year. It is concluded that the Power Authority plan for the development of power at Niagara Falls, depending upon complicated and delicate regulation of the Niagara River and the coordination of this energy with the St. Lawrence power through a vast new transmission network, is proposed too far in advance of the market's ability to consume this surplus energy. The completion of this plan so far ahead of the market would endanger the entire financial structure of the power utility systems of the state.

The proposal to restore the beauty of Niagara Falls through the installation of corrective works at a cost of some $1,750,000, as suggested by the Special International Niagara Board, is believed to be sound. This program would eventually permit a further diversion of 10,000 cfs on each side of the border for power purposes. Utilization of this diversion could be timed with the increase of power demand by first using it through existing stations on each side and later by construction of additional plants to utilize the full head available at that section.

While it is admitted that some savings would accrue to some power consumers in New York State if the St. Lawrence plan were adopted in accordance with the demand for power, nevertheless, as pointed out in the navigation section of this report, such savings would be entirely outweighed and absorbed by related losses accruing to labor and industry in New York from the seaway.

It can only be concluded that the proposition for the development of St. Lawrence power, as an adjunct to the seaway features, is entirely untenable.

(See Major Findings immediately following Introduction).

THE END

APPENDIX A

The Proposed Treaty of 1938

The President of the United States of America and His Majesty the King of Great Britain, Ireland and the British dominions beyond the seas, Emperor of India, in respect of the Dominion of Canada,

Recognizing the Great Lakes-St. Lawrence basin as a great natural resource of the two peoples, offering them enormous advantages in the way of economical transportation and cheap electric power, and

Taking account of the fact that the full advantages to be derived by the two peoples from this resource can only be secured to them through its cooperative development under a comprehensive plan based on full recognition of the mutual interests involved, and

Recognizing that the completion of a deep waterway, not less than twenty-seven feet in depth, for navigation from the interior of the Continent of North America through the Great Lakes and the St. Lawrence River to the sea with the development of the water power incident thereto, would result in marked and enduring benefits to the agricultural, manufacturing and commercial interests of both countries, and

Considering further that the project has been studied and found feasible by the International Joint Commission, the Joint Board of Engineers, and by national advisory boards, and

Recognizing the desirability of effecting a permanent settlement of the questions raised by the diversion of waters from or into the Great Lakes System, and

Recognizing the primary obligation of the Governments of the United States and Canada to preserve and enhance the scenic beauties of the Niagara Falls and River, as recommended by the Special International Niagara Board, and, consistent with that obligation, to provide for the most efficient utilization and equitable apportionment of all water available for the development of hydro-electric power in that area,

Have decided to conclude a treaty for the above-mentioned purposes, and to that end have named as their respective plenipotentiaries:

The President of the United States of America:

His Majesty the King of Great Britain, Ireland and the British dominions beyond the seas, Emperor of India, for the Dominion of Canada:

Who, after having communicated to each other their full powers, found in good and due form, have agreed upon the following Articles:

For the purposes of the present Treaty, unless otherwise expressly provided, the expression:

(a) "International Joint Commission" means the commission established pursuant to the provisions of the Boundary Waters Treaty of 1909;

(b) "Joint Board of Engineers" means the board appointed pursuant to an agreement between the Governments following the recommendation of the International Joint Commission, dated the 19th December 1921;

(c) "Great Lakes System" means Lakes Superior, Michigan, Huron (including Georgian Bay), Erie and Ontario, and the connecting waters, including Lake St. Clair;

(d) "St. Lawrence River" means the river known by that name and includes the river channels and the lakes forming parts of the river channels from the outlet of Lake Ontario to the sea;

(e) "International boundary" means the international boundary between the United States of America and Canada as established by existing treaties;

(f) "International Section" means that part of the St. Lawrence River through which the international boundary line runs;

(g) "Canadian Section" means that part of the St Lawrence River which lies wholly within Canada and which extends from the easterly limit of the International Section to the high seas;

(h) "International Rapids Section" means the easterly portion of the International Section extending from Chimney Point to the village of St. Regis;

(i) "Governments" means the Government of the United States of America and the Government of the Dominion of Canada;

(j) "Countries" means the United States of America and Canada;

(k) "Special International Niagara Board" means the board appointed by the two Governments in 1926 to ascertain and recommend ways and means to preserve the scenic beauty of the Niagara Falls.

Article I

The High Contracting Parties agree to establish and maintain a Great Lakes-St. Lawrence Basin Commission, hereinafter referred to as the Commission, consisting of not more than ten members of whom an equal number shall be appointed by each Government. The duties of the Commission shall be:

(a) To prepare plans for the construction of works in the International Rapids Section in accordance with one of the projects described in the Report of the Joint Board of Engineers with Appendices, dated July 13, 1927, with such modifications as may be agreed upon by the Governments, provided that such modifications do not increase the proposed total cost of the project as estimated in that Report, with a view to providing a navigation channel, not less than twenty-seven feet deep, together with the most suitable works for the development of power;

(b) Upon the approval of the plans by the Governments, to prepare a schedule allocating the construction of the recommended works in the International Rapids Section to the Governments on such a basis that each Government shall construct the works within its own territory or an equivalent proportion of the works in the International Rapids Section;

(c) To approve all contracts entered into on behalf of either Government for the recommended works in the International Rapids Section;

(d) To supervise the construction of the works and to submit reports to the Governments from time to time, and at least once each calendar year, on the progress of the works;

(e) Upon the completion of the works, to certify to the Governments that they meet the specifications of the plans drawn by the Commission and approved by the Governments;

(f) To perform the other duties assigned to it in this Treaty;

(g) To serve as an advisory body to the Governments for the purpose of coordinating all plans for the comprehensive utilization of the entire Great Lakes-St. Lawrence Basin for navigation and power as envisaged in this Treaty.

The Commission shall have the authority to employ engineers, lawyers, experts and employees generally, and to make such other expenditures as may be necessary to carry out the duties herein set forth. It shall have the authority to avail itself of the services of such governmental agencies, officers and employees of either country as may be made available.

The Governments agree to permit the entry into their respective countries, within areas immediately adjacent to the Niagara River and the International Section to be delimited by an exchange of notes, of personnel employed by the Commission or employed in the construction of the works, and to exempt such personnel from the operation of their immigration laws and regulations within the areas to be delimited. They also agree within such areas to exempt from customs duties, excise or sales taxes, or other imposts, all supplies and materials to be used in connection with the construction of the works, as well as all supplies and materials purchased by the Commission for its official use.

The Governments shall, by an exchange of notes, prescribe rules and regulations for the conduct of the Commission. They may, by the same means, extend or abridge its powers and duties, reduce the number of members (provided that there must always be an equal number appointed by each Government) and, upon completion of its duties, terminate its existence.

Article II

With respect to works in the International Rapids Section, the Government of Canada agrees, in accordance with plans prepared by the Commission and approved by the Governments,

(a) to construct or arrange for the construction of the works allocated to Canada by the Commission and to operate and maintain the works situated in the territory of Canada;

(b) to construct or arrange for the construction of the works required for rehabilitation on the Canadian side of the boundary.

The Government of Canada agrees further that, not later than six years after the date of the initiation of construction of Canadian works for additional power under this treaty and, in any event, not later than December 31, 1949, it will provide for the necessary deepening of the New Welland Ship Canal, and for the completion of the essential links in the Canadian Section of the deep waterway to the sea, including canals of the required depth in the Soulanges and Lachine areas of the St. Lawrence River.

Article III

With respect to works in the International Rapids Section, the Government of the United States agrees, in accordance with the plans prepared by the Commission and approved by the Governments,

(a) to construct or arrange for the construction of the works allocated to the United States by the Commission; and to operate and maintain the works situated in the territory of the United States;

(b) to construct or arrange for the construction of the works required for rehabilitation on the United States side of the international boundary;

(c) to provide, as required by the progress of the works, funds for the construction of all works in the International Rapids Section except the following:

(1) Power house superstructures, machinery and equipment for the development of power;

(2) Works required for rehabilitation on the Canadian side of the international boundary; and

(3) Any side canals and locks that may be constructed on the Canadian side of the international boundary.

The Government of the United States agrees further to provide, not later than the date of the completion of Canadian links in the deep waterway, for the completion of the works in the International Rapids Section of the St. Lawrence River, and of the works in the Great Lakes system above Lake Erie which will constitute essential links in the deep waterway to the sea.

Article IV

The High Contracting Parties agree:

(a) that they may, in conformity with the general plans adopted for the project in the International Rapids Section, construct or arrange for the construction in their respective territories of such power houses, machinery and equipment as may be desired for the development of water power and at such time or times as may be most suitable in terms of their respective power requirements;

(b) that, in view of the need for coordination of the plans prepared by the Commission for general works in the International Rapids Section with plans for the development of power in the respective countries, the Commission shall arrange with any agency in either country, which may be authorized to develop power in the International Rapids Section, for the engineering services necessary for the designing of the power works;

(c) that, except as modified by the provisions of Article VIII (d), the quantity of water diverted for the production of power in the International Rapids Section shall be equally divided between the two countries; and, upon completion of the works, the quantity of water utilized during any daily period for the production of power on either side of the international boundary in the International Rapids Section shall not exceed one-half of the flow of water available for that purpose during such period;

(d) that, during the construction and upon the completion of the works provided for in the International Rapids Section, the flow of water out of Lake Ontario into the St. Lawrence River shall be controlled and the flow of water through the International Section shall be regulated so that the navigable depths of water for shipping in the Harbor of Montreal and throughout the navigable channel of the St. Lawrence River below Montreal, as such depths now exist or may hereafter be increased by dredging or other harbor or channel improvements, shall not be injuriously affected by the construction or operation of such works.

Article V

The High Contracting Parties agree, that the construction of works under the present treaty shall not confer upon either of them proprietary rights, or legislative, administrative or other jurisdiction in the territory of the other, and that the works constructed under the provisions of this treaty shall constitute a part of the territory of the country in which they are situated.

Article VI

The High Contracting Parties agree that they may, with the approval of the Commission, proceed at any time to construct, within their own respective territories, alternative canal and channel facilities for navigation in the International Section or in waters connecting the Great Lakes, and that they shall have the right to utilize for this purpose such water as may be necessary for the operation thereof.

Article VII

The High Contracting Parties agree that the rights of navigation accorded under the provisions of existing treaties between the United States of America and His Britannic Majesty shall be maintained notwithstanding the provisions for termination contained in any of such treaties, and declare that these treaties confer upon the citizens or subjects and upon the ships, vessels and boats of each High Contracting Party, rights of navigation in the St. Lawrence River, and the Great Lakes System, including the canals now existing or which may hereafter be constructed.

Nothing in this Article or in any other Article of this Treaty shall be construed as infringing or impairing, in any way, the sovereignty of the United States of America over Lake Michigan.

Article VIII

The High Contracting Parties, recognizing their common interest in the preservation of the levels of the Great Lakes System, agree:

(a) 1. That the diversion of water from the Great Lakes System, through the Chicago Drainage Canal, shall be reduced by December 31, 1938, to the quantity permitted as of that date by the decree of the Supreme Court of the United States of April 21, 1930;

2. In the event of the Government of the United States proposing, in order to meet an emergency, an increase in the permitted diversion of water and in the event that the Government of Canada takes exception to the increase, the matter shall be submitted, for final decision, to an arbitral tribunal which shall be empowered to authorize, for such time and to such extent as is necessary to meet such emergency, an increase in the diversion of water beyond the limits set forth in the preceding sub-paragraph and to stipulate such compensatory provisions as it may deem just and equitable; the arbitral tribunal shall consist of three members, one to be appointed by each of the Governments, and the third, who will be the Chairman, to be selected by the Governments;

(b) That no diversion of water, other than the diversion referred to in paragraph (a) of this Article, from the Great Lakes System or from the International Section to another watershed shall hereafter be made except by authorization of the International Joint Commission;

(c) That each Government in its own territory shall measure the quantities of water which may at any point be diverted from or added to the Great Lakes System, and shall place the said measurements on record with the other Government semi-annually;

(d) That, in the event of diversions being made into the Great Lakes System from watersheds lying wholly within the borders of either country, or in the event of the diversion of rivers into the International Section above their present points of confluence, the exclusive rights to the use of waters equivalent in quantity to any waters so diverted shall, notwithstanding the provisions of Article IV (c) be vested in the country diverting such waters, and the quantity of water so diverted shall be at all times available to that country for use for power below the point of diversion, so long as it constitutes a part of boundary waters;

(e) That the Commission shall undertake a study of the desirability of compensation and regulatory works in the Great Lakes System; and, upon the approval by the Governments of any such works, shall prepare plans for their construction and recommend to the Governments an equitable allocation of their cost. The Governments shall make arrangements by an exchange of notes for the construction of such works as they may agree upon.

Article IX

The High Contracting Parties, recognizing their common interest in preserving the scenic beauty of the Niagara Falls and Rapids, through preventing erosion and ensuring unbroken crestlines, and the prescribing of limits to the diversion of water from the River, agree:

(a) That the Commission shall prepare and submit to the Governments plans for works in the Niagara River to distribute and control the waters thereof to ensure unbroken crestlines on both the American and the Canadian Falls and to preserve and enhance their scenic beauty, taking into account the recommendations of the Special International Niagara Board. The Governments, after the adoption of final plans for the project in the International Rapids Section, shall make arrangements by an exchange of notes for the construction of such works in the Niagara River as they may agree upon, including provision for temporary diversions of the waters of the Niagara River for the purpose only of facilitating their construction. The cost of such works in the Niagara River shall be borne by the Governments in equal moieties.

(b) That, upon the completion of the works authorized in this Article, diversions of the waters of the Niagara River above the Falls from the natural course and streams thereof additional to the amounts specified in Article 5 of the Boundary Waters Treaty of January 11, 1909, may be authorized and permitted by the respective governments of the United States and Canada to the extent and in the manner hereinafter provided:

(1) The United States may authorize and permit additional diversion within the State of New York of the waters of said river above the Falls for power purposes, in excess of the amount specified in Article 5 of the Boundary Waters Treaty of January 11, 1909, not to exceed in the aggregate a daily diversion at the rate of five thousand cubic feet of water per second;

(2) Canada may authorize and permit additional diversion within the Province of Ontario of the waters of said river above the Falls for power purposes, in excess of the amount specified in Article 5 of the Boundary Waters Treaty of January 11, 1909, not to exceed in the aggregate a daily diversion at the rate of five thousand cubic feet of water per second;

(c) That, upon installation of the works authorized in this Article, the Commission shall proceed immediately to test such works and to report and certify to the Governments the effect of such works under a wide range of conditions and to make recommendations respecting diversions of water from Lake Erie and the Niagara River with particular reference to preserving perpetually the scenic beauty of the Falls and Rapids, to the requirements of navigation in the Great Lakes System and to the equal and equitable diversion and efficient utilization of the waters. On the basis of the Commission's reports and recommendations the High Contracting Parties may by an exchange of notes and concurrent legislation determine the methods by which these purposes may be attained.

Article X

The High Contracting Parties agree:

(a) That each Party is hereby released from responsibility for any damage or injury to persons or property in the territory of the other, which may be caused by any action authorized or provided for by this Treaty;

(b) That each Party will assume the responsibility for and expense involved in the acquisition of any lands or interests in land in its own territory which may be necessary to give effect to the provisions of this Treaty.

Article XI

This Treaty shall be ratified in accordance with the constitutional methods of the High Contracting Parties. The ratifications shall be exchanged in Washington or in Ottawa as soon as practicable and the Treaty shall come into force on the day of the exchange of ratifications.

In faith whereof the respective plenipotentiaries have signed this Treaty in duplicate and have hereunto affixed their seals.

Done at .... the .... day of ....

in the year of our Lord .. ..

(SEAL)   (SEAL)

APPENDIX B

Source of Rates Used in Economic Study

IMPORTS

COMMODITY	FROM	TO	ROUTE	RATE PER TON	SOURCE
Bananas	New Orleans	Chicago	Rail	$17.40	Emerson's 8-J
,, ...	Jamaica	Montreal	Ocean	15.00	Contract
Sugar...............	Havana	New York	,,	2.00	,,
,, ...	New Orleans	Chicago	Barge	8.20	Federal Barge Line 69-M
,, ...	,, ,,	Minneapolis	,,	11.00	,, ,, ,, ,, ,,
,, ...	New York	Chicago	Motorship	5.00	Contract
,, ...	,, ,,	Duluth	,,	5.20	,,
Coffee	Rio de Janeiro	New Orleans	Ocean	7.63	,,
,, ...	,, ,, ,,	New York	,,	7.63	,,
,, ...	New Orleans	Chicago	Barge	6.60	Federal Barge Line 2-J
,, ...	New York	,,	Motorship	5.40	Contract
Kaolin.............	Liverpool	Philadelphia	Ocean	4.20	,,
,, ...	Philadelphia	Cincinnati	Rail	6.80	Curletts 23-J
,, ...	Cleveland	,,	,,	4.80	Jones 480
Rubber.............	Straits	New York	Ocean	18.00	Contract
,, ...	New York	Akron	Rail	8.60	Curletts 23-J
,, ...	Cleveland	,,	,,	3.00	Jones 480

EXPORTS

COMMODITY	FROM	TO	ROUTE	RATE PER TON	SOURCE
Grain.................	Duluth	London	New York	4.08	{ Average for 9 years
,, ...	,,	,,	Montreal	4.13	{ Lake Carriers Association
Flour.................	Minneapolis	New York	Rail	7.60	Kipps 2942 & Jones 245
,, ...	,,	Chicago	,,	2.60	Kipps 2942
,, ...	Buffalo	New York	Barge	1.06	Contract
,, ...	Chicago	,, ,,	Motorship	5.20	,,
,, ...	New York	Liverpool	Ocean	3.40	,,
Iron & Steel............	Chicago	New York	Rail	7.48	Jones 3281
,, ,, ...	,,	,, ,,	Water	3.25	Contract
,, ,, ...	New York	Rio de Janeiro	Ocean	4.50	,,
Agricultural Implements..	Chicago	New York	Motorship	3.75	,,
,, ,, ..	New York	Liverpool	Ocean	5.00	,,
,, ,, ..	Chicago	New York	Rail	9.00	Jones 218-L
Autos	Detroit	New York	Rail	9.60	Jones 218-L
,, ...	New York	Liverpool	Ocean	4.40	Contract
Packing House Products..	Chicago	New York	Motorship	4.00	,,
,, ,, ,, ..	New York	Liverpool	Ocean	7.00	,,
,, ,, ,, ..	Chicago	New York	Rail	9.40	Jones 218-L

INDEX

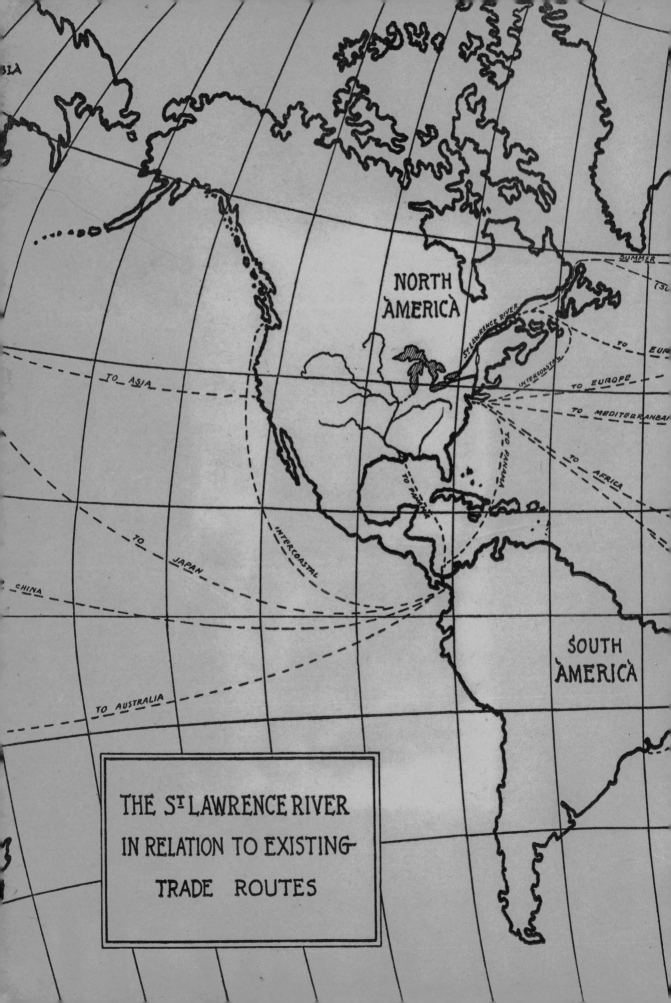

THE ST LAWRENCE RIVER
IN RELATION TO EXISTING
TRADE ROUTES